RECIPES F

Arthritis and Rheumatism

Delicious recipes to relieve the symptoms of arthritis and rheumatism

ALKMINI AND LEON CHAITOW

Thorsons
An Imprint of HarperCollins*Publishers*

Thorsons
An Imprint of HarperCollins*Publishers*
77–85 Fulham Palace Road,
Hammersmith, London W6 8JB

1160 Battery Street,
San Francisco, California 94111–1213

First published by Thorsons 1996

1 3 5 7 9 10 8 6 4 2

© Alkmini and Leon Chaitow 1996

Alkmini and Leon Chaitow
assert the moral right to
be identified as the authors of this work

A catalogue record for this book
is available from the British Library

ISBN 0 7225 3317 9

Typeset by Harper Phototypesetters Limited,
Northampton, England
Printed and bound in Great Britain by
Caledonian International Book Manufacturing Ltd, Glasgow

All rights reserved. No part of this publication may be
reproduced, stored in a retrieval system, or transmitted,
in any form or by any means, electronic, mechanical,
photocopying, recording or otherwise, without the prior
permission of the publishers.

Contents

Chapter 1	Arthritis and Rheumatism – What Are They?	1
Chapter 2	Relieving Arthritis and Rheumatism Through Diet	10
Chapter 3	Dos and Don'ts and Special Notes	27
Chapter 4	Before We Start – Some Basic Recipes and Preparation Tips	35
Chapter 5	Breakfasts	44
Chapter 6	Salad Dressings	53
Chapter 7	Salads	57
Chapter 8	Dips	74
Chapter 9	Soups	80
Chapter 10	Side Dishes	89
Chapter 11	Vegetarian Main Courses	105
Chapter 12	Main Meals with Fish	144
Chapter 13	Main Meals with Chicken and Turkey	155
Chapter 14	Desserts	160
Index		169

I dedicate this book to my sister, Katherine Metallinos-Kiess with warm affection, and in loving memory of our parents Stavros and Antigoni Metallinos

Alkmini Chaitow

1

Arthritis and Rheumatism – What Are They?

EXPERTS BELIEVE that about one person in six suffers from a rheumatic condition, sometimes very severely but the majority only mildly. Because there are so many different types of rheumatic condition, with widely different symptoms (although all involve pain, stiffness and inflammation), we need to briefly list some of these and their known or possible causes. These conditions include osteoarthritis, rheumatoid arthritis, gout, ankylosing spondylitis, SLE, fibromyalgia ('muscular rheumatism'), and others.

A WORD ABOUT 'INFLAMMATION'

Tissues that are damaged or irritated become inflamed. We take this fact for granted and we also accept that it is common sense to get rid of the inflammation, using medication or cold compresses, ice and so on, because inflammation hurts and is unpleasant. But is this way of thinking and acting sensible?

Inflammation is, in fact, evidence that the body's defence and repair mechanisms are in action. Medical treatment of rheumatism and arthritis almost always involves taking non-steroidal anti-inflammatory drugs (NSAIDs – the drugs commonly used in the treatment of most joint and muscle problems to ease symptoms) and, in severe cases, SAIDs, such as cortisone, as well.

Research over the past 25 years or so into the effects of NSAIDs has shown that while they certainly do ease symptoms, reducing pain and swelling as the inflammation is calmed down, people who take them end up with far worse joint problems than do people with arthritis who do not take them. The reason for this is complicated, but, at its simplest, these problems are the result of the NSAIDS interfering with the repair of cartilage and, in many cases, actually speeding up its destruction. NSAIDS also produce severe side-effects, often taking the form of stomach problems, headaches, dizziness and hearing noises (tinnitus).

Does this mean that we should do absolutely nothing about the often unbearable symptoms of rheumatism and arthritis? No, but using drugs to 'switch off' what is in fact the body's repair mechanism may be too drastic a method and gentler ways, which deal with the causes of the problem, plus encouraging healing and calming pain, but which do not interfere with the natural repair process, may offer a better way forward. Following the dietary suggestions to treat arthritis given in this book fits into such a sensible, safe and often very effective approach.

Rheumatic conditions, which almost always involves inflammation, swelling, stiffness and pain in the joints of the body, occur in a number of different forms. The main ones are the following.

OSTEOARTHRITIS

This disease affects men and women in equal numbers. Individual joints become affected as a result of damage or 'wear and tear', resulting in a gradual destruction of the smooth, pearly cartilage that covers the ends of bones. In its normal state, cartilage allows the joint to move and the bones to glide over each other easily. This ease of movement is gradually lost as osteoarthritis develops.

Most elderly people have some osteoarthritic changes, although for most this level of change causes no more than a mild degree of stiffness that is usually worse in the morning and results in no actual handicap.

The likeliest age for the onset of osteoarthritis is from the mid-forties onwards. Various factors that can contribute to the development of osteoarthritis are:

- excess weight
- the degree and type of physical activity (work and sport) you do – jarring or repetitive stress to the joints is especially likely to be harmful
- hormonal imbalances
- a history of physical injury to the area
- the normal ageing process.

Diet can also influence osteoarthritis – both in its early stages and when it is established – by encouraging or reducing the inflammatory processes, which always play a part in the development of the disease. Diet can also encourage a regeneration of damaged cartilage and joint tissues. Diet will be discussed in more detail later in this section.

RHEUMATOID ARTHRITIS

This disease affects many joints simultaneously, progressively destroying the joint cartilage. The most affected joints are the knuckles, wrists, elbows, knees and feet. The joints may become very swollen and distorted over time as the surface of the joint is increasingly damaged. It is usual for joints to be affected symmetrically rather than on only one side of the body. Many other tissues can also be affected by this condition, including the skin, heart and the lymph glands which both filter wastes from the body and manufacture defensive cells for the immune system.

Women are far more likely than men to develop rheumatoid arthritis (three women develop it for every man) and the condition usually starts gradually, but can sometimes come on very abruptly, between the ages of 20 and 40. A significant number of children also develop rheumatoid arthritis (there is some evidence of a link between this and abnormal reactions to rubella vaccines).

Rheumatoid arthritis is often accompanied by a low-grade fever and, like other autoimmune conditions (those where the body's defence system is attacking itself), it is thought to involve a genetic tendency. Various theories also suggest that it originates due to the influence of microorganisms (bacteria and yeasts have both been blamed, particularly a microorganism commonly associated with cystitis in women – proteus), allergies, emotional stress, lifestyle factors or some combination of these. A more recent theory suggests that a changed ecology of the bowel, possibly involving abnormal bacterial overgrowth, may be involved in which the normal flora (friendly bacteria) and the intestinal mucous membrane may be damaged, allowing undesirable substances (toxins, allergens and so on) to be 'malabsorbed' into the bloodstream. Some of these substances have been shown to chemically resemble tissues in the joints, thus, the theory goes, causing the immune system to attack healthy tissues, mistaking them for undesirable antigens.

This theory, which links the infection and allergy theories, has much support from leading rheumatologists and is similar to what seems to be happening in ankylosing spondylitis, another arthritis-like autoimmune condition, described below.

As we will see, dietary strategies can and have been used to minimize the effects of this potentially crippling condition.

GOUT

The causes of gout, which mostly affects men, remain something of a mystery, although it is clear that complicated disturbances involving some of the delicate metabolic processes of the body are usually involved, often of a kind associated with anaemia and kidney problems. The onset of gout is usually sudden, with the first joint of the big toe being the first place affected. The pain and swelling of gout results from the presence in the tissues of excessive amounts of uric acid, which forms crystals and induces the inflammation. The excessive uric acid can be the result of either too much being formed by the body, which is so for the majority of cases, or, in around a third of people affected, too little uric acid being cleared from the system. A genetic predisposition to gout has been identified in some people. However with gout, as is the case with all rheumatic conditions, diet can influence the progress of the disease significantly – for good or ill. In other words, the 'wrong' foods can make things worse and the right ones can help to reduce the symptoms and encourage healing.

ANKYLOSING SPONDYLITIS

This is a slowly progressive degenerative condition resulting from a similar mistaken attack by the immune system on the body's own tissues. Once again, as in rheumatoid arthritis, bacterial overgrowth in the intestinal tract (usually of an organism known as klebsiella) is blamed by researchers as being the cause of the problems.

The symptoms of ankylosing spondylitis are stiffness and pain, usually commencing in the lower back but spreading to the rest of the spine and leading to a fusion of the spinal joints into a bamboo-like rigidity, the spine taking on a marked forward curve. Dietary changes have been shown in medical studies in London to be capable of slowing or stopping the progression of this disease, usually involving a low intake of sugar and fat and a high intake of complex carbohydrates – vegetables, whole grains and pulses.

SYSTEMIC LUPUS ERYTHEMATOSUS

A chronic inflammatory disease, also involving an auto-immune process, its main symptoms are extreme fatigue, arthritis-like changes and pain in the joints, which become swollen, as well as fever and a skin rash, which is most commonly on the face (butterfly rash) and the muscles may become extremely sensitive. Lupus affects young women more than any other group and is more common in people of African descent than Caucasian.

Dietary intervention can be helpful in reducing the inflammatory processes, and this will be outlined in the next chapter.

FIBROMYALGIA

As well as the above rheumatic conditions in which *joints* are the major target, there are also a number of purely *muscular* rheumatic conditions. The most prominent of these is fibromyalgia, which used to be called fibrositis, a generalized muscular condition involving pain, stiffness and profound fatigue.

DIET AND ARTHRITIS

We know from the personal experience of many thousands of people with arthritis, as well as from excellent medical research, that diet can have a powerful influence on arthritic conditions. Diet can make symptoms worse when it is poor or unbalanced, yet help relieve the symptoms, sometimes dramatically, when it is correct for the person involved.

Because an arthritic condition can be aggravated by many nutritional factors, there is no single dietary approach that will help everyone. However, there is evidence that a nourishing demi-vegetarian pattern, which may include fish and poultry, is the most likely to be helpful.

Proven nutritional connections with arthritis are:

- increased toxicity – possibly caused by a disturbed bowel condition in which poor bowel function can result in putrefactive toxins being formed and absorbed. A diet high in complex carbohydrates can help this

- allergy/sensitivity factors
- an excess in the diet of those foods that 'fuel' inflammation
- a deficiency of vitamins, minerals, amino acids and other nutrients that have an anti-inflammatory influence as these are not being supplied by the food eaten.

The recipes in this book have as their main focus the need to discourage toxicity, inflammation and allergic factors while encouraging nutritional excellence.

In the following chapter, we will briefly explain the factors that can cause problems and tell you some of the best ways in which you can help bring about an improvement in arthritic conditions.

2

Relieving Arthritis and Rheumatism Through Diet

WATCH YOUR WEIGHT

OBVIOUSLY IT IS HELPFUL for anyone with arthritis – especially if the weight-bearing joints such as the feet, ankles, knees, hips and/or spine are affected – to ensure, as far as possible, that any surplus weight is reduced.

As having arthritis may make exercise difficult or impossible, particular care must be taken when choosing what to eat or drink. Where weight is a problem, it is especially helpful to consider quantity as well as quality in what is eaten, without becoming obsessive or cranky about it.

When food is nutritious and 'whole' – as opposed to refined and excessively processed – less needs to be eaten in order to feel satisfied. When convenience and highly processed foods containing 'empty' calories (they taste good but provide little nourishment) form a major part of the diet, weight is likely to increase and health decline. It is important to think about what you eat and choose what will help your body become healthier rather than thwart it.

By using the recipes in this book, you will learn how to make a balanced selection of foods, ensuring that you are actively promoting your own good health, discouraging the arthritis and rheumatism and excess weight, and, most importantly, find that you can do this and simultaneously enjoy delicious food.

REDUCE INFLAMMATION NATURALLY – THE ANTI-INFLAMMATION DIET

Inflammation is both the most obvious source of pain and joint restriction in arthritic conditions and evidence that the body is trying to heal the irritated and damaged joint surfaces and soft tissues. If an informed decision is taken to avoid, or to use only sparingly, NSAIDs (see Chapter 1), then other, gentler methods to reduce inflammation can be beneficial.

The 'raw material' of inflammation (in muscle, a joint, the skin or anywhere else in the body) is arachidonic acid, some of which we synthesize ourselves but most of which we derive from animal fats. Arachidonic acid is turned into inflammatory agents called leukotrienes, and these can be diminished in number, calming inflammation of any sort including arthritis, by reducing or avoiding animal fats and increasing your intake of fatty acids from vegetable and fish sources. Doing this cuts down leukotriene production because the raw materials used to make it are no longer there.

Put simply an anti-inflammation diet calls for you to:

- eat little or no animal fat (dairy, meat and poultry fats) because this increases arachidonic acid levels, leading to more leukotrienes being produced and greater inflammation
- consume more fish and/or more vegetable fatty acid-rich foods (see below) because this also reduces arachidonic acid levels, which means fewer leukotrienes and so less inflammation.

VEGETARIAN AND VEGAN DIETS HELP ARTHRITIS

There are numerous research studies which show that a vegetarian (no meat, poultry or fish) or vegan (no animal products at all) diet can have very beneficial effects on some arthritic conditions. In one research study, 20 people with rheumatoid arthritis followed a vegan diet and also reduced their coffee, tea, spices and sugar intake. After 4 months, 12 of them had shown a significant and sustained improvement.

Whether this change occurred because such a diet eliminates animal fats, removes many allergens (see below) or provides more antioxidant vitamins (discussed later in this chapter) or for some other reason(s), is not clear. What is obvious is that a diet which drastically reduces animal sources of food is a great help to people with arthritis. For example, in a one-year Norwegian trial involving people with severe rheumatoid arthritis, it was shown that by following a strict vegetarian pattern, most symptoms of pain and stiffness improved (sometimes dramatically) and returned once again when the diet changed back to include animal-based foods.

Other antiarthritis diets that have been shown to help many sufferers include that devised by Dr Dong in the USA which stressed the importance of avoiding dairy products. Dairy foods are, of course, another source of animal fats, so it is either because of the reduction in inflammation that tends to follow stopping dairy foods or the possible link between allergy and arthritis (see below) that this approach has proved so successful.

The recipes in this book follow a no meat (or very little indeed), no dairy products (or extremely small amounts)/ vegetarian or demi-vegetarian (no meat, but some fish) strategies towards arthritis control as a result of these findings. Where poultry is included in a recipe, it will be suggested that all skin and fat be removed.

Fish that come from cold-water areas, such as the North Sea, are richest in the oils that antagonize and reduce arachidonic acid production and inflammation. They do not stop it being produced altogether, but calm it down to more acceptable levels, so that the pain and swelling are lessened, but the repair processes are not interfered with.

The fish richest in these helpful oils include herring, sardines, mackerel and salmon. To get the most from these oils, it is suggested that these fish should be eaten twice weekly and more if possible.

Another way of obtaining these oils is by taking 10 to 12 EPA (eicosapentenoic acid) fish oil capsules (available from all pharmacies and healthfood shops) or a tablespoon of cod liver oil daily.

Vegetarians can avoid the need to take fish oil by consuming ample amounts of flaxseed oil (at least two tablespoons daily) and/or evening primrose oil (four 500-mg capsules daily), both of which contain linoleic and linolenic acids, which help to dampen the inflammation process gently, as well as providing other essential nutrients for the body.

The vegetarian option will almost certainly take longer before it is effective in calming symptoms than the more direct fish oil approach, and in severe or chronic cases, some months of persistent supplementation may be needed before benefits are seen. This is often the case when dietary strategies are being used to modify health conditions.

Summary

Eat less (or no) meat and more fish (cold-water varieties) and consume foods rich in, or supplement with, plant sources of essential fatty acids (flaxseed oil, evening primrose oil, borage oil and so on).

ANTIOXIDANT NUTRIENTS FIGHT ARTHRITIS

The process of inflammation involves, among other things (such as leukotrienes, discussed earlier in this chapter), substances called 'free radicals'. These are unstable molecules that can cause damage to other molecules by removing from them one of their atoms. An example of free radical damage is what happens when hydrogen peroxide (bleach or H_20_2) is in touch with hair. H_20_2 literally drags atoms out of the hair, making it change colour. When large quantities of free radicals are present in our bodies, perhaps as a result of a high-fat, high-sugar diet (or toxicity involving heavy metals such as lead or mercury which most of us acquire from atmospheric pollution or dental treatment), a great deal of tissue damage can occur, including some of the problems associated with arthritis. Other examples of free radical damage include cataracts in the eyes, atherosclerosis in blood vessels and the ageing process, in which tissues harden and lose elasticity.

In nature, free radicals are what makes radiation dangerous. In less dramatic ways, they are responsible for the oxidizing processes in which metals rust, rubber perishes and apples and potatoes turn brown when exposed to air. Just as a squeeze of lemon juice onto a freshly cut apple will stop the browning process (because of the antioxidant the juice contains, vitamin C), various nutrients can have an anti-free radical, antioxidant, protective, effect in our bodies.

The main antioxidant substances active in protecting our body tissues and functions include vitamins A, C, E, the minerals selenium and zinc, the amino acids cysteine and methionine, plus the mixture of amino acids and minerals glutathione peroxidase. Many of the foods used in the recipes in this book contain large amounts of these vital protective substances, particularly fresh vegetables and fruits.

Supplementing with an antioxidant combination may also prove to be a useful strategy. For example, there are a number of A, C, E and selenium combination products available from healthfood shops and pharmacies, and one or two tablets taken daily (this is only a guide, read the information on the package carefully for individual product formulation and recommended dosages) would be helpful in easing free radical damage in arthritic joints and tissues.

Some of these nutrients, particularly vitamins A, C and E (as well as zinc and vitamin B_6) are also vital in maintaining and rebuilding cartilage that has been damaged by arthritis.

AVOID FOODS FROM THE NIGHTSHADE FAMILY

Foods derived from plants from the genus *Solanaceae* (nightshade) seem to affect some genetically susceptible people. These plant foods, which include tomatoes, potatoes, aubergines and peppers, contain substances that promote inflammation and slow the repair of damaged joints, as well as encouraging pain and discomfort in muscles.

When over 5000 people with arthritis were asked to avoid these foods, they were monitored for a 7-year period and nearly 75 per cent of them reported a gradual reduction in pain and restriction.

While some of the recipes in this book include foods from these sources, the majority do not, and anyone with an arthritic condition is urged to try excluding these foods for at least one month to see if there is any improvement. If it is not possible to cut them out completely for this length of time, a rotation pattern can be tried. This is explained in the next section of this chapter.

THE CONNECTION BETWEEN ALLERGY AND ARTHRITIS

Many arthritis sufferers have been shown to have food sensitivities or actual allergies that are aggravating or, some say, causing their condition.

There are a number of ways of identifying foods to which we are sensitive. The simplest of all is to just leave out of the diet particular foods or whole families of food (dairy products, for example, or foods from the *Solanaceae* plant family, mentioned above).

When a food is eliminated from the diet, the beneficial effects of its absence (assuming it was causing problems) are usually obvious after five days or so, when all traces of the food are no longer in the body. If things get better when a particular food is not eaten, you can prove that it was causing problems by eating (or drinking) it again several times in 24 hours then watching see whether or not the symptoms reappear over the next day or so. This absolutely identifies culprit foods, allergens.

Once such sources of trouble have been positively identified, they can be left out of the diet altogether or eaten only in a rotation pattern. This means eating the particular food or any food from its 'family' no more than once in five days in order to prevent reactions. Rotation is a compromise between eating the food whenever you wish and not eating it at all.

THREE-WEEK OLIGOANTIGENIC DIET FOR ALLERGY

The oligoantigenic diet was developed at Great Ormond Street Hospital for Sick Children, London, and at Addenbrooke Hospital, Cambridge, as a means of identifying foods that might be causing or aggravating various conditions. As we saw above, by avoiding foods that may be provoking symptoms for not less than five days, all traces of any of the food will have cleared the system and any symptoms caused by them should have vanished. Symptoms that remain after such an elimination period are either caused by something else altogether (infection, for example) or by other foods or substances.

On reintroduction of the foods in a carefully controlled sequence (called a 'challenge'), symptoms that reappear show themselves to be a reaction to particular foods, so these foods are then eliminated from the diet for a considerable time.

There is some evidence to support the idea that those foods which have become a major part of the human diet since Stone Age times, mainly grains (particularly wheat) of all sorts and dairy products, are the most likely to provoke reactions. All modern processed foods involving any chemicals, colourings, flavourings and so on are also suspect. Many researchers claim that a period on a 'Stone Age diet' allows a whole range of other allergies and health problems to disappear.

The oligoantigenic diet is usually followed for up to three weeks while a careful check is kept on symptoms (pain, stiffness, mobility and so on). If they improve or vanish, then one or more of the foods being avoided may be to blame. Identification and subsequent avoidance of the culprit food(s) depends on whether or not the symptom return on reintroduction (challenge) of the food.

The eating pattern given below is a modified version of the hospital pattern.

To try a modified oligoantigenic exclusion diet, use the following a pattern of eating, either including or excluding the foods listed below, for three weeks.

Fish

Allowed white fish, oily fish
Forbidden All smoked fish

Vegetables

Forbidden potatoes, tomatoes, peppers, aubergines (people with bowel problems are asked to avoid beans, lentils, Brussels sprouts and cabbage as well)

Fruit

Allowed bananas, peeled pears, pomegranates, papaya, mango
Forbidden all fruits except the five allowed ones

Cereals

Allowed rice, sago, millet, buckwheat
Forbidden wheat, oats, rye, barley, corn

Oils

Allowed sunflower, safflower, linseed, olive
Forbidden corn, soya, 'vegetable', nut (especially peanut)

Dairy

Allowed none
Forbidden cow's milk and all its products, including yogurt, butter, most margarines, all goat, sheep and soya milk products, eggs

Drinks

Allowed some herbal teas, such as chamomile and peppermint
Forbidden tea, coffee, fruit squashes, citrus drinks, apple juice, alcohol, tap water, carbonated drinks, milk

Miscellaneous

Allowed sea salt
Forbidden yeast products, chocolate, preservatives, *all* food additives, herbs, spices, honey, sugar of any sort

If benefits are felt after this fairly drastic exclusion, a gradual introduction of one food at a time, leaving several days between each reintroduction, will allow you to identify those foods that should be left out altogether as the troublesome foods will cause symptoms to reappear when they are added to the diet. If a reaction occurs, that food is eliminated for at least six months and a five-day period of no further experimentation is followed (to clear the body of all traces of the offending food) after which testing (challenge) can start again.

To make sense of this may require expert help. Several (up to three) weeks on a 'Stone-age' or oligoantigenic diet might dramatically improve a wide range of symptoms of allergies. Identifying what those foods are requires patience.

If you wish to try single exclusions, the families of foods (or individual foods) that should be assessed should include the nightshade family (as suggested above), dairy foods (especially cow's milk products), grains (especially wheat), soya products, eggs, citrus foods.

Cautionary note: It is not unusual when a food to which you are strongly allergic and that you have been consuming regularly (daily as a rule) is stopped for you to feel 'withdrawal' symptoms for a week or so, including flu-like symptoms and marked mood swings, anxiety, restlessness and so on. If this happens, it is suggested that you consult a qualified nutritionist, naturopath or homoeopath for advice. This can be a strong indication that whatever you have eliminated from the diet is responsible for a 'masked' allergy, which may be producing many of your symptoms.

REDUCING BOWEL (AND GENERAL BODILY) TOXICITY

Toxins formed in the bowel (aided by the influence of undesirable bacteria and yeasts) may, in some people, pass into the bloodstream and cause toxic or allergic reactions that then start or aggravate arthritic conditions. The activity of some organisms, such as *Candida albicans* (a yeast), can cause damage to the delicate lining of the bowel. This allows a breach of the boundary between the body proper and the self-contained world of the digestive tract. Then, substances that would otherwise have been kept out can enter the bloodstream. The main result of the breaking of the intestinal barrier is that undigested proteins from foods, as well as toxic wastes from bacterial or yeast infestation, may begin to circulate in the bloodstream, causing a wide variety of symptoms.

One of the most effective ways of improving the health of the bowel is to focus attention on the billions of friendly bacteria that inhabit the intestines and offer us major benefits (manufacturing vitamins, recycling various essential substances, such as hormones, detoxifying the bowel) in return for the home and food we offer them. In fact, they (mainly *Lactobacillus acidophilus* in the small intestine and *Bifidobacteria* in the colon) do all these things when they are in good health. When they are damaged by antibiotics or steroid medication or become sluggish in their work because of a high-fat and high-sugar diet (which suits their enemies – yeasts such as *Candida albicans* – but not them), they are less effective in their detoxification and manufacturing work and may actually be driven out of their territory by undesirable bacteria (such as klebsiella and proteus, for example; see Chapter 1) or yeasts. In such circumstances, symptoms of variable diarrhoea and constipation as well as bloating may become regular features, along with an increasing degree of fatigue and a host of minor physical and mental symptoms.

It is not within the scope of this book to give comprehensive advice regarding normalizing a bowel in which such overgrowth has taken place, but you can find out more from my books *Candida Albicans – Could Yeast be Your Problem?* (Thorsons, 1995) and *Principles of Fasting* (Thorsons, 1996). In general, the sort of diet the recipes in this book encourages will be an ideal way in which to start to normalize the bowel when it is unhealthy (this is known as bowel dysbiosis).

Some particularly useful strategies include making sure that a great deal of garlic is eaten (there is a lot of this in some of the recipes in this book) and olive oil (also a common feature in the recipes) as both have significant antifungal effects. Additionally, it is wise to take a high-quality acidophilus and bifidus supplement each day (any good healthfood shop will have this).

Our general well-being, as well as that of the friendly bacteria, improves if bowel function is regular. The high fibre content of vegetables and the foods in the recipes in this book should ensure that daily bowel movements take place. If this fails to happen, then one or two tablespoons of flaxseed (linseed) taken with water, on its own, swallowed unchewed, away from mealtimes, should encourage regularity.

OTHER DIETARY HINTS

- You will notice that one of the foods that appears quite frequently in the recipes is ginger. This is not just a chance matter. Ginger has been shown in medical studies to have beneficial effects in people with arthritis and muscular pain (fibromyalgia) – as well as being good for the digestion and immune function. Ginger is useful in this way both when taken as food and when taken in capsule form as a supplement.
- The enzyme bromelaine, which is derived from the pineapple plant, has gentle anti-inflammatory effects when it is taken away from mealtimes and helps the body to digest proteins when it is taken at mealtimes. Taking supplements of 500 mg several times a day is recommended as an anti-inflammatory.
- Apple cider vinegar has been shown to be a helpful aid in arthritic conditions. Taking two teaspoons in warm water with each meal is suggested. It can also be used on salad as a dressing.

Supplements

Based on the results of much research, the following listings are given not as recommendations but for general information. Anyone wishing to take supplements as part of their treatment of their arthritis should first take responsible professional advice, especially if they are already taking prescription medication.

Supplements Helpful for Osteoarthritis

Vitamin B_3 (niacinamide) – between 500 and 2000 mg daily
Vitamin B complex – one 100-mg tablet daily
Vitamin B_5 (pantothenic acid, as calcium pantothenate) – 500 mg daily
Vitamin C – 500 mg daily, plus 500 mg bioflavonoids
Vitamin E – 900 iu daily
Glycosaminoglycans (raw material of cartilage) from green-lipped mussel extract
Calcium – 2000 mg daily
Magnesium – 1000 mg daily
L-cysteine (amino acid) – for one month, take 2 g daily, away from meals, plus three times as much vitamin C

Supplements for Rheumatoid Arthritis

Vitamin B_5 (pantothenic acid, as calcium pantothenate) – 500 mg four times a day
Vitamin C – 500 to 2000 mg daily, plus 500 mg bioflavonoids
Selenium – 100 micrograms daily
Zinc – three 20-mg tablets daily
Glycosaminoglycans (raw material of cartilage) from green-lipped mussel extract.
Omega–3 fatty acids (fish oils) – total of up to 2 g daily in 180-mg capsules

Omega-6 fatty acids (evening primrose oil) – 1 g four times a day
Calcium – 2000 mg daily
Magnesium – 1000 mg daily
L-cysteine (amino acid) – for one month, take 2 g daily, away from meals, plus three times as much vitamin C

Acidophilus and Bifidobacteria – not less than one billion organisms of each daily (in the form of capsules or powder, never tablets)

By using appropriate supplements in combination with a sensible modification in your diet – using the principles explained so far and the recipes that follow – you can make a major contribution to recovery from the worst effects of many arthritic and rheumatic problems.

3

Dos and Don'ts and Special Notes

AVOID FANATICISM!

A GENERAL CAUTION is given at this stage: obsessive attention to every detail of the information in this book is be avoided – exercise your common sense in applying the guidelines. The occasional lapse – eating some of the undesirable foods, for example – will almost certainly not make you ill or your symptoms worse. It is your *usual* pattern of eating and life that is important, not the odd deviation.

You will recall from earlier that one of the main things advocated was avoiding foods from the *Solanacaea* family, such as tomatoes, potatoes, peppers and aubergines. They therefore appear only sparsely in the recipes in this book, but they *do* show up now and then – mainly tomatoes and in small amounts. Do not be perturbed about this. We thought long and hard about including any of these foods at all in the recipes (it would have been quite easy to avoid them altogether) and eventually decided that by including a few, we could signal to you that you should allow yourself to be a bit lax on this point at times without feeling guilty.

DAIRY FOODS AND FATS

As we saw earlier, other foods that should, in the main, be avoided are those containing animal fats, which means all meat, most poultry and any fat-rich dairy foods. This is because of the profound influence fats have on inflammation. Therefore, there are only a few dairy foods in some of the recipes in this book and these are always of the virtually fat-free kind. In contrast, fish oils are known to be a helpful kind of fat and so you will find quite a few recipes that feature the fruits of the sea.

OILS

It will not take you long to notice that olive oil is frequently used in the recipes. There are many reasons for this, but, briefly, it is a monounsaturated oil, almost never causes allergic reactions and has major health-enhancing properties. As an alternative, safflower oil is also a good choice and so in the recipes that call for oil, you will see 'olive or vegetable oil' in the ingredients. This simply means for you to use olive oil if you can or safflower oil if olive oil is not available or another vegetable oil if even safflower is not available.

If you do use olive oil, then remember that the first, cold-pressed virgin olive oil is the best and really should be used for dressings, when cooking is not involved, to appreciate its taste and avoid losing precious nutrients that are lost when it is heated. When you use olive oil in cooking, a less expensive, ideally cold-pressed olive oil is adequate. Butter or a butter substitute is used in only one recipe, for shortcrust pastry, as you are unlikely to eat it more than once in a while, which will do you no harm.

SPECIFIC FOOD SENSITIVITIES

Individually, any of the foods we eat may cause some undesirable reaction. Which foods are causing the problems need to be identified by careful detective work, using exclusion and challenge patterns as suggested in the previous chapter. Wheat, dairy foods and eggs are commonly implicated and should be tested in this way. The recipes in this book try to provide as wide a range as possible of well-tolerated foods.

EGGS

Some well-known experts suggest that egg yolks can be an irritant for those who have arthritis and, although a few recipes are included in this book that use eggs, most of these use only egg whites, just a few calling for whole eggs. This is yet another food for which a caution rather than a prohibition should operate. You should not be concerned if you find yourself eating eggs more than once a week or so, unless, of course, you discover that eggs do have a negative effect on your condition and it will then be up to you to decide on your best course of action.

SALT – YES OR NO?

The recipes that follow do not often mention salt in the ingredients. This is because of a belief widely held by naturopathic medical practitioners and many medical experts that salt is an undesirable element if you have an arthritic condition.

Salt substitutes exist, most notably potassium chloride (salt is sodium chloride). These are available from most healthfood shops and pharmacies as it is generally advised that we cut down our intake of salt, though this is particularly important for people with high blood pressure.

VEGETARIAN – YES OR NO?

Many of the savoury dishes described in the following pages are vegetarian (they contain no meat or fish) and some are vegan (contain no animal products at all) as these patterns of eating are known, following extensive trials, to help people with arthritis to function better and have less pain. This is *not* meant to be taken as a suggestion that you should become vegetarian but, rather, that you incorporate into your regular pattern of eating meals and foods that are delicious, easy to prepare and will ease you towards eating patterns that are most likely to reduce your pain and other symptoms effectively.

TOFU

One of the best alternatives to animal protein is this soya bean product. This bland 'soya cheese' has little taste in itself, but takes on the flavours of foods with which it is cooked. It is therefore commonly added to the vegetarian stews and pies described in this book. The inclusion of tofu is almost always described as optional in the recipes, but it is highly recommended.

GARLIC

This wonderful herb is much in evidence in the recipes in this book, so it is worth a word or two here regarding both the many benefits it offers and its sometimes pungent aroma.

Its proven health benefits include its being an antiseptic, antifungal and antiparasitic agent, which means it can help to heal an unhealthy digestive system (important in arthritis), lower high blood pressure, reduce cholesterol levels, help reduce cattarhal congestion, improve the body's absorption of some of the B vitamins and control high sugar levels in diabetes.

As to the smell, well, yes, it does have a pungent odour when raw, but this virtually vanishes when it is cooked (unfortunately so do some of its benefits) and almost all of the times it is used in this book, it is cooked so the smell should not be an issue. If this ever does present a problem, though, then eating a few sprigs of raw parsley will sweeten the breath.

Different types of garlic are available, those with white and those with pink skins. The white-skinned ones are stronger in both flavour and odour. When buying garlic, test to see whether or not the heads are fresh by pressing the cloves. If on pressure they feel spongy, the head of garlic is old and drying out. Choose heads of garlic that have firm cloves.

Quantities

You can expect a head of garlic to yield between 12 and 14 cloves, not unnaturally, the larger the head, the larger the cloves. The large cloves are easier to peel than small ones. A large crushed or chopped clove will produce approximately 1 to 1½ teaspoons of garlic.

Spring garlic is easy to grow and is delicious. Just break up a head of garlic and press the individual cloves into soil in a windowbox, pot or in the garden 5 cm (2 in) or so apart and then water regularly. Within weeks, you will have delicate spring onion-like shoots. When they are 12 to 15 cm (5 to 6 in) tall, harvest them by pulling them out of the ground. Use these chopped – the bulb, stem, leaves and all – in a salad or cooked with vegetables (artichoke for example) or in a soup.

SERVING COOKED VEGETABLES

Whether steamed, lightly boiled or stir-fried, individual vegetables, such as fennel, cauliflower, courgettes, spring greens, wild vegetables (see below) and so on, can have their flavour enhanced markedly by using a few simple tactics.

1. As an alternative to serving them hot straight after cooking, consider serving the vegetables at room temperature, as they do in Southern Europe. To do this, after being cooked in whichever is the most convenient way (steaming retains most of the nutrient value as does stir-frying), the vegetables should be placed in a serving dish and allowed to cool to room temperature.
2. Just before being served (hot or cold), dress the vegetables with olive oil (virgin, first cold pressing) and lemon juice. The flavour of vegetables is better when served in this way, especially when served at room temperature.
3. A few cloves of garlic cut into paper thin slices and scattered on vegetables such as greens, adds a dramatic additional flavour.

WILD VEGETABLES

The nutritional value as well as the amazing flavours of wild vegetables remain a mystery to most people. Try exploring the possibility of adding comfrey, nettle tops (just the tender young leaves or shoots), dandelion or mustard greens to your diet. Incidentally, cultivated dandelion greens are available at many Greek, Italian, Spanish, Arab/Middle Eastern and other ethnic food shops. If you harvest your own, choose sites free of traffic pollution if possible and away from sites regularly visited by dogs, for obvious reasons. The greens should be well washed, and either steamed or boiled for about 15 minutes until tender. Drain and serve with lemon juice and dressed with olive oil. They are amazingly rich in nutrients and will do wonders for the bowels.

COOKING BEANS

Many of the recipes ask for beans to be soaked overnight, cooked for a while and then for the water to be changed and other particular instructions. If followed, these suggestions will ensure that the enzymes which cause flatulence are removed, making sure that there is no bloating – a common bean byproduct!

GINGER

Ginger features in a number of the recipes that follow, both in the form of a purée (now widely available) and as fresh root ginger. This versatile herb has specific benefits to offer people with arthritis and muscle pain and is also wonderfully helpful for anyone with digestive problems. We urge you to use it abundantly.

4

Before We Start – Some Basic Recipes and Preparation Tips

HOW TO PREPARE GLOBE ARTICHOKES

1. Cut away the stem close to the head and remove most of the leaves until the tender ones are reached.
2. Cut the artichoke into two halves, cutting it from the top to the bottom.
3. With a grapefruit knife, remove the choke, which is the hairy covering of the heart of the vegetable.
4. Squeeze the juice of half a lemon into a saucepan and add 850ml (30fl oz/3¾ cups) of cold water.
5. Rub the newly exposed surfaces of the artichoke halves with the other half of the lemon before placing them in the saucepan with the lemon and water (this mixture prevents browning – oxidation – of the exposed surfaces).
6. The tender leaves and the peeled stem (after rubbing with the lemon half) may also be placed in the saucepan and used in subsequent recipes.

7. Keep the artichoke (and stem and leaves if keeping) in the lemon water until just before you need them in the recipes.

PREPARING RICE

The only rice used in the recipes in this book is the vitamin- (B_1, B_2, B_6) and mineral- (magnesium, potassium, iron) rich unpolished brown kind. Avoid at all costs the devitalized and almost nutrient-free polished white kind – it provides empty calories and little else.

Different kinds of rice need to be cooked in quite different ways, but, in general, the following guidelines are valid.

1. If you are using a pressure cooker, which is recommended, then follow the manufacturer's instructions.
2. When cooking in the usual way, rinse the rice in tepid water and place it in a saucepan with a lid (a cast iron pan is best for cooking rice if you are not using a pressure cooker). Add water, ensuring that there is approximately 4cm (1½ in) of water above the surface of the rice. This translates into the following ratios of rice to water, although in dry climates more water and in humid climates less water may be needed. Remember that the more water is used, the softer the rice will be after cooking. A reasonable guide to quantities would be:

for 395g (14oz/2 cups) of rinsed and drained brown rice, use 1200ml (40fl oz/5 cups) of water for cooking (but see 5 and 6 below). This quantity would serve 4 people.

3. Once the water containing the rice is boiling, reduce the heat until it is very gently simmering, then cover, ensuring that the lid of the pot fits tightly.
4. Approximately 45 to 55 minutes is required to cook whole rice, but this may vary depending on the hardness of the water being used. Do not stir the rice during the cooking as this may cause it to become sticky.
5. As rice absorbs water as it cooks, and different varieties absorb more or less water, it is not possible to give a figure for the quantity of water required that will always hold true. Start with the amount given above and check the pan from towards the end of the cooking time to see if you need to add more.
6. If additional water is required – say, if the rice is clearly not cooked and the water has virtually all been absorbed – some boiling water should be added a little at a time so that the simmering process is not disturbed.
7. When cooked, toss the rice gently using a wooden spoon or spatula and allow it to stand in a bowl (wooden is best) for several minutes before serving.

Brown Rice and Sesame Seeds

For this delicious combination, prepare the rice as, but dry roasted sesame seeds are added to the rice at the beginning of the cooking process. The seeds are prepared as follows.

1. For the quantity of rice described above, you need 85g (3oz/½ cup) unhulled sesame seeds.
2. Wash and drain the sesame seeds and place them in a pan and dry roast them over a medium heat shaking the pan or stirring constantly as they can burn easily.
3. When they begin to turn brown, remove the pan from the heat and allow to cool.
4. Sprinkle the seeds onto the rice before cooking it as given above. Alternatively, add the dry roasted seeds to the rice after it is cooked and just before serving.

SHORTCRUST (PIE) PASTRY

This recipe will make enough pastry to line a 20-cm(8-in) diameter pie dish and make a lid for the pie, which would serve 4 as a main course.

You can usefully make several batches at once when you have some time as this pastry freezes well.

Metric/Imperial		*American*
225g/8oz	wholemeal/wholewheat plain/all-purpose flour	2 cups
pinch	salt substitute	pinch
125g/4½oz	nut butter	1 cup
15–30g/ 1–1½oz	polyunsaturated margarine	2–2½ tbsp
about 120ml/ 4fl oz	cold water, to mix	about ½ cup

1. Sift the flour and salt substitute together into a bowl, then rub (cut) the nut butter and margarine into the flour by hand until the mixture resembles bread-crumbs.
2. Add water gradually and mix, adding just enough for the mixture to form into a stiff dough.
3. Roll the pastry out with a floured rolling pin (or floured bottle) to a thickness of approximately 5mm (¼ in).

MUSHROOM SAUCE FOR SPAGHETTI OR RICE

This sauce is an ideal base from which all kinds of variations can be developed to serve with rice or pasta. Unlike most such sauces, it does not include tomatoes and so is ideal if you have arthritis and wish to avoid members of the *Solanaceae* family, for the reasons given earlier. Also, as pasta is readily available that is made from foods other than wheat – rice, corn, soya beans and so on – those sensitive to wheat can also enjoy marvellous Mediterranean dishes without aggravating their bodies.

If you wish and are not sensitive to dairy products, a sprinkling of grated hard low-fat cheese over the sauce and pasta is very good.

You can make several batches of this sauce at a time or use some and freeze the rest as it freezes well.

Serves 4

Metric/Imperial		*American*
990g/2lb	button mushrooms	2lb
285ml/10fl oz	olive/vegetable oil	1½ cups
2	medium onions, quartered	2
6	garlic cloves, peeled	6
pinch	cayenne pepper	pinch
2	bay leaves, crushed	2
2 tsp	dried basil	2 tsp
120ml/4fl oz	dry white wine	½ cup
5 twists	freshly ground black pepper	5 twists
500ml/16fl oz	cold water	2 cups
to taste	salt substitute	to taste

1. Wipe the mushrooms, then place them in a food processor or blender and chop until they are in large breadcrumb-size pieces.
2. Transfer the mushrooms to a saucepan.
3. Place the onion pieces, garlic, basil and bay leaves in a food processor or blender and process until the mixture has a creamy consistency.
4. Add the onion, garlic and herb mixture to the mushrooms, add the remaining ingredients and mix everything together well.
5. Bring to the boil, then simmer over a low heat until all the water evaporates (approximately 40 minutes).
6. Serve hot on spaghetti or rice or use in the recipes later in this book.

PINE NUT AND ALMOND PESTO SAUCE

This remarkable variation on traditional pesto can be used on and in a huge range of rice, pasta and vegetable dishes. Make some and you will wonder how you lived without it!

Try adding half this sauce to freshly cooked, drained pasta for three people, tossing the pesto and pasta together to coat the pasta with the pesto before serving on a platter with the remainder of the pesto spooned on top.

Serves 3 to 4

Metric/Imperial		*American*
55g/2oz	fresh basil	2 cups
55g/2oz	fresh parsley	2 cups
70g/2½oz	pine nuts	½ cup
85g/3oz	ground almonds	1 cup
170ml/6fl oz	olive/vegetable oil	¾ cup
5	garlic cloves, crushed	5
to taste	salt substitute	to taste
4 twists	freshly ground black pepper	4 twists

1. Wash the basil and parsley very well, then drain and chop finely in a food processor or blender.
2. Then, having rinsed out the food processor or blender, grind the pine nuts.
3. Place the basil, parsley, pine nuts and ground almonds in a blender together with the oil, garlic, salt and pepper and blend until you have a thick sauce.

NON-DAIRY BÉCHAMEL SAUCE

A simple white sauce that does not include dairy products is ideal for those with arthritis or who are sensitive to these foods. It can be used in so many ways, and is particularly good with Stuffed Cabbage Leaves (page 136).

Metric/Imperial		*American*
240ml/8fl oz	vegetable cooking water	1 cup
4 tbsp	wholemeal/wholewheat self-raising flour	4 tbsp
90ml/3fl oz	olive/vegetable oil	⅓ cup
425ml/15fl oz	soya milk	2 cups
2	whole eggs	2
5 twists	freshly ground black pepper	5 twists
to taste	salt substitute	to taste

1. Place the flour and oil in a frying pan over a moderate heat and stir constantly until they are well mixed.
2. Add to this mixture small amounts of soya milk and vegetable cooking water, each in turn, until they are all added, stirring constantly so you have a smooth, glossy, lump-free sauce.
3. Take the pan off the heat and add the egg, blending these into the sauce.
4. Add the pepper and salt substitute to taste, then return to the heat to bubble for a minute. Serve.

5

Breakfasts

EXOTIC POMEGRANATE AND PASSION FRUIT BREAKFAST

Of all the fruits in the world, the ones that produce the fewest 'sensitivity reactions' (see Chapter 1) are pears, pomegranates and passion fruit. The last two of these form the basis of this exotic, enzyme-rich, energy-packed start to the day.

Serves 1

Metric/Imperial		*American*
1	pomegranate	1
2	passion fruit	2
30g/1oz	sunflower seeds	¼ cup
30g/1oz	flaked/slivered almonds	¼ cup
218g/7oz	muesli mixture (sugar-free)	1¾ cups
120ml/4fl oz	soya milk or juice of your choice	½ cup
1 or 2 tbsp	flaxseed oil, optional*	1 or 2 tbsp

1. Prepare the pomegranate by cutting a slice off the stem end. Then, slice into sections lengthwise and pull the sections apart. Remove the seeds and the juicy flesh around them singly or in groups, placing them in a bowl, and discard the skin and inedible yellow membranes.
2. Place all the dry ingredients in another bowl.
3. Cut the passion fruit in half and empty the juice and seeds on to the dry ingredients.
4. Add the prepared pomegranate.
5. Add the soya milk or juice and flaxseed oil, if using, mix well and serve.

* Flaxseed oil provides a huge quantity of essential fatty acids, similar to those provided by fish oils, and so is extremely useful for people with arthritis. It is available from better healthfood shops and should be kept refrigerated.

STONE AGE BREAKFAST

This recipe is based on what we know to have been the diet of Stone Age people. Grains were not on the menu, but eaten instead were those foods that would have been easily available to our hunter-gatherer ancestors and which were energy rich and nourishing. These foods are very well tolerated by people with food sensitivities and allergies and this recipe contains such foods.

Serves 1

Metric/Imperial		*American*
1 tbsp	sunflower seeds	1 tbsp
1 tbsp	pumpkin seeds	1 tbsp
½ tbsp	pine nuts	½ tbsp
½ tbsp	linseeds	½ tbsp
½ tbsp	sesame seeds	½ tbsp
30g/1oz	freshly ground almonds or walnuts or pecans	⅓ cup
30g/1oz	chopped unsulphured dried apricots or peaches or sultanas/golden seedless raisins	¼ cup
1	dessert apple, grated, or pear, diced	1
½ cup or 1	mango or papaya, peeled and diced	½ cup or 1
1 or 2 tbsp	flaxseed oil, optional*	1 or 2 tbsp

1. The night before, place the seeds and pine nuts in a bowl and barely cover with water. Leave to soak overnight.
2. Just before breakfast, add the ground nuts, dried and fresh fruit and flaxseed oil, if using.

Variation

A tablespoon or 2 of either wheat flakes, millet or oats can be added to the seed mixture before it is soaked overnight, if there is no sensitivity to grains.

* Flaxseed oil provides a huge quantity of essential fatty acids, similar to those provided by fish oils, and so is extremely useful for people with arthritis. It is available from better healthfood shops and should be kept refrigerated.

SWISS POWER BREAKFAST

Do not eat this breakfast if you are sensitive to wheat or grains.

This breakfast is based on a traditional Swiss recipe and is used in many health spas throughout Europe. It provides enormous energy, plenty of fibre and has great nutritional value.

Serves 1

Metric/Imperial		*American*
1 tbsp each of 3 or 4 of these	whole wheat, rye, oats, barley and/or millet	1 tbsp each of 3 or 4 of these
2 tbsp	wheat bran	2 tbsp
2 tbsp	unsulphured raisins	2 tbsp
340ml/12fl oz	water	1½ cups
1 or 2 tbsp	flaxseed oil, optional*	1 or 2 tbsp
1	apple or pear, stewed or puréed	1

Slow (overnight) method

1. The night before, coarsely grind the grains.
2. Place all the remaining ingredients, except the flaxseed oil, in a saucepan with the water.
3. Bring to the boil and allow to simmer for 7 to 10 minutes.
4. Remove from the heat and wrap the pan in a blanket or newspapers and allow to stand for several hours.

5. If the resulting porridge is too loose, use a little less water next time.
6. Serve hot with the flaxseed oil, if using, as well as freshly made or bought unsweetened apple or pear purée or stewed (no sugar added) pears or apples.

Alternative (rapid) method

This second, uncooked version retains more nutritional value but requires more chewing and is not recommended for people with irritable bowels.

1. Place all the ingredients, except the flaxseed oil, in a saucepan and add boiling water to cover.
2. Allow to stand for half an hour (this should be enough time for the cereals to absorb the liquid) before serving as above, with the flaxseed oil, apples or pears (puréed or stewed).

* Flaxseed oil provides a huge quantity of essential fatty acids, similar to those provided by fish oils, and so is extremely useful for people with arthritis. It is available from better healthfood shops and should be kept refrigerated.

OMELETTE

This is adapted from Dr Dong and his co-author Jane Banks' recipe from *New Hope for the Arthritic*, which they wrote some 20 years ago. Dr Dong was very strictly against the use of all dairy foods, meat and egg yolks in his diet for those with arthritis and very pro fish. His 'eggless' omelette makes a useful breakfast dish as it is nutritious and tasty and yet leaves out the egg yolks.

Serves 1

Metric/Imperial		*American*
30g/1oz	mushrooms, sliced	½ cup
30g/1oz	celery, finely sliced	½ cup
2	egg whites, unbeaten	2
2 tbsp	olive or safflower oil	2 tbsp
to taste	salt substitute	to taste

1. Using a non-stick frying pan and the small amount of oil suggested, slightly sauté the mushrooms and celery (or any other vegetable ingredient you fancy, such as onions) to just soften them, then remove them from the pan and place into a bowl which contains the unbeaten egg whites.
2. Gently stir the vegetables into the egg whites until well mixed, then add a pinch of salt substitute.
3. Pour this mixture into the still heated frying pan and allow to cook until it is just browning before turning it and cooking the other side in the same way. Serve straight away.

POMEGRANATE AND WHEAT

This dish is eaten cold and needs to be prepared the night before as the wheat has to be cooked for almost an hour. Avoid if you are sensitive to wheat.

Serves 2–4

Metric/Imperial		*American*
285g/10oz	whole wheat grains	2½ cups
2	pomegranates	2
70g/2½oz	raisins or sultanas/golden seedless raisins	½ cup
85g/3oz	walnut halves	1 cup
2 tbsp	natural/plain, live yogurt, optional	2 tbsp

1. Rinse the wheat well, picking out any grit or small stones, then place it in saucepan and cover well with cold water. Allow to stand overnight.
2. Discard the soaking water and replace with fresh water to cover the wheat. Bring to the boil and allow to simmer until tender (40 minutes to an hour).
3. Prepare the pomegranate as described on page 45.
4. Drain the wheat and place in a serving bowl, then add all the remaining ingredients and the yogurt, if using.

HIGH-FIBRE MILLET, OATS AND FRUIT BREAKFAST

This high-fibre, quickly cooked, millet-based breakfast provides an ideal start to the day.

Serves 1

Metric/Imperial		*American*
3 tbsp	millet, washed	3 tbsp
500ml/16fl oz	water	2 cups
pinch	salt substitute	pinch
1	peach, apricot, apple or pear, peeled and diced	1
2 tbsp	unsulphured raisins	2 tbsp
2 tbsp	rolled/jumbo oats	2 tbsp
1 tbsp	chopped walnuts or almonds, optional	1 tbsp
½ tsp	ground cinnamon, optional	½ tsp

1. Place the millet plus half the water and the pinch of salt substitute in a saucepan. Cover, bring to the boil and simmer for 15 minutes.
2. Now add the remaining water, fresh as well as dried fruit and oats. Bring to the boil once more, then allow to simmer, covered, for a further 10 minutes, stirring periodically.
3. Allow to cook uncovered for a final 2 minutes.
4. Serve, topped with the chopped nuts and a sprinkling of cinnamon, if using.

6

Salad Dressings

BORIS'S MINT AND HONEY SALAD DRESSING

This dressing was devised by Boris Chaitow, the famous pioneer of dietary health promotion, for use on the vast salads he ate daily throughout his almost 90 years of active life.

Makes sufficient to dress a large salad for 1

Metric/Imperial		*American*
3 tbsp	sunflower oil	3 tbsp
1 tbsp	lemon juice	1 tbsp
1 tsp	honey	1 tsp
2	garlic cloves, crushed	2
2 tbsp	fresh mint leaves, chopped	2 tbsp

1. Mix the oil and lemon juice in a bowl.
2. Dissolve the honey in a cup with a little hot water, then add it to the oil and lemon mixture, together with the crushed garlic and the chopped mint leaves.
3. Mix all the ingredients together thoroughly and keep refrigerated until required.

SPICY DRESSING

Among the ingredients of this wonderful salad dressing are some important antiarthritis nutrients, perhaps the most important of which is cider vinegar, followed closely by olive oil.

Makes sufficient for a large salad to serve 3 or 6 side salads

Metric/Imperial		*American*
240ml/8fl oz	olive or sunflower oil	1 cup
90ml/3fl oz	cider vinegar	⅓ cup
pinch	cayenne pepper	pinch
1 tbsp	brown sugar	1 tbsp
1½ tsp	ready-made mustard	1½ tsp
4 twists	freshly ground black pepper	4 twists
to taste	salt substitute	to taste

1. Place all the ingredients in a bowl or clean screw-top jar and mix well.

GARLIC AND CIDER VINEGAR DRESSING

Makes sufficient for a large salad to serve 3 or 6 side salads

Metric/Imperial		*American*
3 tbsp	cider vinegar	3 tbsp
1 tsp	French mustard	1 tsp
2	garlic cloves, crushed	2
1 tsp	fresh basil, parsley or thyme, chopped, or	1 tsp
1 tsp	dried marjoram or tarragon	1 tsp
3 twists	freshly ground black pepper	3 twists
to taste	salt substitute	to taste
90ml/3fl oz	cold-pressed, virgin olive oil	⅓ cup

1. Blend together the cider vinegar, mustard, garlic, herbs, pepper and salt substitute.
2. Mix this into the oil and blend well together.

7

Salads

CABBAGE, CAULIFLOWER AND AVOCADO SALAD

Serves 2

Metric/Imperial		*American*
115g/4oz	cabbage, finely shredded	1 cup
115g/4oz	cauliflower florets, chopped	1 cup
15g/½oz	parsley, chopped	½ cup
55g/2oz	onion, finely chopped	⅓ cup
170g/6oz	avocado pear	1 cup
2 tbsp	lemon juice	2 tbsp
115g/4oz	fat-free cottage cheese or yogurt, optional	½ cup
1 or 2	bananas, sliced, optional	1 or 2

1. Place the cabbage and cauliflower in a bowl together with the parsley and chopped onion.

2. Peel the avocado, remove the stone and dice the flesh. Pour the lemon juice over the dice to prevent them going brown.
3. Add the avocado to the cabbage and cauliflower mixture and combine. Serve with the dressing of your choice (see pages 53–56 for some ideas). If desired and if you are not sensitive to dairy products, top with the fat-free cottage cheese or yogurt. Alternatively the sliced banana tastes wonderful with this salad. Add just before serving to avoid it discolouring.

MIDDLE EASTERN CELERY SALAD

Celery, which is highly recommended by experts for arthritic conditions, forms the basis of this refreshing, nutritious and satisfying meal. The pine nuts, dates, sultanas (golden seedless raisins) and walnuts (which can be replaced by pecans or almonds if desired) make an energy-rich combination. Serve as a side salad or as a main meal with wholemeal (wholewheat) bread or a baked sweet potato.

Serves 2 as a main meal, 4 as a side salad

Metric/Imperial		*American*
8	celery sticks	8
85g/3oz	pine nuts	½ cup
5	fresh dates, depipped, chopped	5
55g/2oz	sultanas/golden seedless raisins	⅓ cup
85g/3oz	walnut halves	1 cup
1	dessert apple, peeled and diced	1
215ml/7½fl oz	vinaigrette sauce (see Spicy Dressing, page 55, or Garlic and Cider Vinegar Dressing, page 56)	1 cup
2 tbsp	sunflower seeds, optional	2 tbsp
2 tbsp	pumpkin seeds, optional	2 tbsp

1. Clean the celery sticks, removing all strings, and chop into 1.25-cm (½-in) lengths.
2. Place the celery pieces in a salad bowl and add all the remaining ingredients, including the seeds, if using, and toss together.

CHICKPEA (GARBANZO) AND GINGER SALAD

Few foods have such varied food value as do chickpeas (garbanzos). Rich in magnesium, potassium, iron and, of course, protein, they taste good and are versatile, too.

The technique used to cook them in this recipe ensures that the gas-forming enzymes are removed so that they can be easily digested.

Serve at room temperature as a salad or hot as a side dish.

Serves 2

Metric/Imperial		*American*
285g/10oz	dried chickpeas/garbanzos	1¼ cups
240ml/8fl oz	olive oil	1 cup
115g/4oz	onion, grated	⅔ cup
2 tsp	dried rosemary	2 tsp
85g/3oz	root ginger, peeled and freshly grated	½ cup
4 twists	freshly ground black pepper	4 twists
to taste	salt substitute	to taste

1. Soak the chickpeas (garbanzos) in water overnight, ensuring that the water covers them completely.
2. The next day, before cooking the chickpeas (garbanzos), discard the soaking water and rinse them thoroughly, removing any froth which has formed.
3. Place the chickpeas (garbanzos) in a saucepan, cover with fresh water and bring to the boil.

4. Meanwhile, boil a kettle of water.
5. Allow the chickpeas (garbanzos) to simmer for 20 minutes before removing them from the heat, discarding the water and replacing it with the water you have just boiled (it must still be boiling), covering the chickpeas (garbanzos).
6. Add all the remaining ingredients and simmer until tender, or until all the water has evaporated, stirring from time to time.

MEDITERRANEAN CHICKPEA (GARBANZO) SALAD

Serves 2

Metric/Imperial		*American*
200g/7oz	dried chickpeas/garbanzos	1 cup
2 tbsp	dried rosemary	2 tbsp
90ml/3fl oz	olive/vegetable oil	⅓ cup
3 twists	freshly ground black pepper	3 twists
to taste	salt substitute	to taste

1. Soak the chickpeas (garbanzos) overnight.
2. The next day, discard the soaking water and rinse thoroughly, removing any froth that has formed.
3. Place the chickpeas (garbanzos) in a saucepan, cover with fresh water and bring to boil. Simmer for 20 minutes, skim and discard froth that forms.
4. Meanwhile, bring a kettle of water to the boil.
5. Discard the chickpeas (garbanzos) cooking water and replace it with the fresh, still boiling water from the kettle.
6. Now add all the remaining ingredients.
7. Simmer, stirring now and again, until all the water has evaporated, by which time the chickpeas (garbanzos) should be tender.
8. Serve at room temperature as a side dish.

BUTTER (LIMA) BEAN SALAD

The combination of butter (lima) beans with the herbs and other ingredients in this salad makes it a nutritional treasure house of particular value to anyone on a full or demi-vegetarian diet.

Serves 2–3 as a side dish

Metric/Imperial		*American*
200g/7oz	dried butter/lima beans	1 cup
115g/4oz	onions, diced	½ cup
1 tsp	dried oregano	1 teaspoon
55g/2oz	spring onions/scallions, sliced	⅓ cup
115g/4oz	celery sticks, sliced	1 cup
120ml/4fl oz	olive/vegetable oil	½ cup
1 tbsp	lemon juice or cider vinegar	1 tbsp
8	stoned/pitted large black olives	8
4 twists	freshly ground black pepper	4 twists
to taste	salt substitute	to taste

1. After washing, soak the butter (lima) beans overnight in water.
2. The next day, rinse the beans thoroughly, place in a saucepan and add fresh cold water to cover.
3. Bring to the boil and simmer for 20 minutes, removing froth.
4. Meanwhile, bring a kettle of water to the boil.

5. Discard the cooking water and replace with the fresh, still boiling water and a little salt substitute (to taste). Simmer until tender, adding more hot water if necessary.
6. Remove the pan from the heat, drain and then empty the beans into a salad bowl and add all the remaining ingredients, except the olives.
7. Toss gently, adding the olives before serving. Serve warm or after letting it cool to room temperature.

GREEN PEASANT SALAD AND DRESSING

This variation on a traditional Southern European peasant salad avoids peppers and tomatoes and offers a choice of cheese or tofu as the source of protein.

Serve this salad with a savoury dish as a side salad or together with wholemeal (wholewheat) bread and walnuts as a main meal in its own right.

Serves 1 or 2 as a main course,
2 to 4 as a side dish

Metric/Imperial		*American*
3	radishes, halved	3
8	cucumber slices	8
3	lettuce leaves, shredded by hand	3
3	spring onions/scallions, chopped	3
½	onion, finely sliced	½
85g/3oz	red or white chicory/endive	1 cup
2	celery sticks, sliced	2
30g/1oz	fresh parsley, chopped	½ cup
30g/1oz	fresh mint, chopped	½ cup
½ tsp	dried oregano	½ tsp
2 tbsp	olive/vegetable oil	2 tbsp
4 tsp	cider vinegar	4 tsp
8	black olives	8
115g/4oz	white cheese, cubed or crumbled, or tofu, cubed	1 cup

2 tbsp	sunflower seeds, optional	2 tbsp
2 tbsp	pumpkin seeds, optional	2 tbsp

1. Place radishes, cucumber, lettuce, both kinds of onions, chicory (endive), celery, parsley and mint in a salad bowl.
2. Prepare the dressing by mixing the oregano, oil and cider vinegar well together in a screw-top jar, then drizzle over the salad before gently tossing the salad (ideally using wooden salad servers) to ensure that the dressing evenly coats all the vegetables.
3. Sprinkle the olives, cheese or tofu and the seeds, if using, over the salad.

Note to Cooks

Ingredients that would add zest and could either complement or replace the herbs and vegetables listed in this recipe include:

- 3 to 4 leaves of rocket
- 3 to 4 sprigs of watercress
- 2 to 3 leaves of dandelion (young tender central leaves not the old outer ones)
- 2 to 3 radish leaves (young, tender ones).

GREEN LEAF AND HERB SALAD

Serves 2 as a side dish

Metric/Imperial		*American*
85g/3oz	cos/romaine lettuce	1 cup
15g/½oz	basil leaves	¼ cup
45g/1½oz	rocket/arugula or watercress	1½ cups
30g/1oz	parsley	½ cup
7g/¼oz	coriander/cilantro	¼ cup
15g/½oz	mustard and cress	½ cup
7g/¼oz	fresh mint	½ cup
3 tbsp	olive oil	3 tbsp
90ml/3fl oz	lemon juice	⅓ cup
to taste	salt substitute, optional	to taste
2 tbsp	sunflower seeds, optional	2 tbsp
2 tbsp	pumpkin seeds, optional	2 tbsp

1. Clean and wash all the salad and herb ingredients and shred into small pieces by hand. Place in a salad bowl.
2. Mix the olive oil, lemon juice and salt to taste together well in a screw-top jar, drizzle over the salad and then mix it in well.
3. Serve as a side salad with any savoury dish, sprinkling the seeds over the top just before serving, if using.

MIXED VEGETABLE COOKED SALAD

Salads are usually thought of as consisting of raw vegetables. For those with more delicate digestions and for a change, a cooked salad makes an interesting dish.

This recipe avoids all the members of the undesirable nightshade family and should be very well tolerated by people with food sensitivities.

Serves 1

Metric/Imperial		*American*
1	carrot, well washed and sliced	1
115g/4oz	French/fine green beans, trimmed	1¼cups
½	fennel bulb, cut into large pieces	½
1	globe artichoke (page 35)	1
115g/4oz	peas	⅔ cups
1	celery stick, strings removed, sliced	1
1	small beetroot, cooked and diced	1
5	black olives	5
1	small Spanish onion, sliced	1
2 tbsp	olive oil	2 tbsp
1 tbsp	cider vinegar	1 tbsp
½ tsp	oregano	½ tsp
to taste	salt substitute	to taste

1. Place the carrot, beans, fennel, artichoke and peas in a steamer and steam for 10 minutes.
2. Add the celery and steam for 5 more minutes.
3. Spoon the cooked vegetables on to a serving dish and add the diced beetroot, olives and onion.
4. Shake the remaining ingredients together in a screw-top jar, then pour over the vegetables. Serve hot or cold.

Note to Cooks

This salad tastes just as good, perhaps even better, if it is eaten cold and dressed with lemon juice.

ROOT SALAD

While not consisting entirely of root vegetables, this salad calls for the predominant presence of four mineral-rich ingredients – beetroot (beet), carrots, celeriac (celery root) and radishes – along with a variety of additional salad treasures.

Serves 2 to 3 as a main meal

Metric/Imperial		*American*
140g/5oz	tender carrots	5oz
140g/5oz	celeriac/celery root	5oz
4	radishes	4
70g/2½oz	cucumber	2½oz
55g/2oz	baby courgette/zucchini	2oz
140g/5oz	raw beetroot/beet	5oz
1 tbsp	lemon juice	1 tbsp
90g/3oz	onion, thinly sliced	½ cup
45g/1½oz	firm button mushrooms, thinly sliced	½ cup
85g/3oz	freshly shelled walnuts	1 cup
1 tbsp	sunflower seeds	1 tbsp
1 tbsp	pumpkin seeds	1 tbsp
1	dessert apple, peeled and diced, optional	1
3 tbsp	virgin olive oil	3 tbsp
1½ tbsp	cider vinegar	1½ tbsp
1 tsp	runny honey	1 tsp
1 tsp	ready-made mustard	1 tsp

4 twists	freshly ground black pepper	4 twists
to taste	salt substitute	to taste

1. Clean all the vegetables, which should also be peeled if they are not organic and well washed and/or scrubbed even if they are.
2. Prepare the carrots, celeriac (celery root), radishes, cucumber and courgette (zucchini) by cutting long thin lengthwise strips using a swivel peeler or else grate them.
3. Grate the beetroot (beet) finely, then add the lemon juice to it.
4. Mix all the prepared vegetables in a bowl together with the onion, mushrooms, walnuts, sunflower and pumpkin seeds and the diced apple, if using.
5. Place the oil, vinegar, honey, mustard, pepper and salt in a cup and stir until smooth or into a screw-top jar and shake well.
6. Pour over the salad and toss well just before serving.

ORANGE SALAD

This recipe makes an ideal accompaniment for poultry or a snack meal combined, for example, with fresh walnuts and wholemeal (wholewheat) bread.

Serves 2

Metric/Imperial		*American*
2	navel/seedless oranges*	2
2 tbsp	virgin olive oil	2 tbsp
pinch	salt substitute	pinch
pinch	cayenne pepper	pinch
pinch	paprika	pinch
1	spring onion/scallion, chopped	1

1. Peel the oranges, leaving as much pith as possible (it is vitamin-rich and is known to enhance circulation).
2. With a sharp knife, cut the oranges into even, medium-thickness slices.
3. Arrange each the slices of each orange on a serving plate and pour over the olive oil, then sprinkle over the seasoning and spring onion (scallion).

* If 'blood' oranges are available, these can be used – carefully depipped – instead of standard navel oranges.

8

Dips

HUMMUS

This traditional Turkish/Middle Eastern dish can be served with soup as a side dish or as a party dip together with Tzatzicki (page 77) or Walnut and Garlic Dip (page 79). It is also ideal served as a main meal with wholemeal (wholewheat) toast (a complete protein combination) and a mixed salad or as a starter with celery or carrot sticks.

Serves 4–6

Metric/Imperial		*American*
285g/10oz	dried chickpeas/garbanzos	1½ cups
2 sprigs	dried or fresh rosemary	2 sprigs
285ml/10fl oz	virgin olive oil	1⅓ cups
210ml/7½fl oz	lemon juice	1 cup
to taste	salt substitute	to taste
5 twists	freshly ground black pepper	5 twists
8 (or more)	garlic cloves, crushed	8 (or more)
3 tbsp	tahini (ready made)*	3 tbsp

1. Wash the chickpeas (garbanzos) and soak overnight in cold water to cover.
2. In the morning, the chickpeas (garbanzos) will have swollen to virtually double their size. Discard the soaking water, rinse them well and place them, with fresh water to cover by at least 2½ cm (1in), in a saucepan and slowly bring to the boil.
3. Before the water comes to the boil, white froth will appear and this should be skimmed off. When the water is boiling and all froth has been removed, add the rosemary and simmer until the chickpeas (garbanzos) are tender (this can take from 30 to 90 minutes, depending on the hardness of the water and the quality of the chickpeas/garbanzos).
4. When the chickpeas (garbanzos) are tender, add half the olive oil, a quarter of the lemon juice, salt substitute to taste and the pepper and continue to simmer.
5. When the chickpeas (garbanzos) are really soft, drain (reserving at least 210ml (7½fl oz/1 cup) of the cooking liquid) and remove them from the saucepan and place in a food processor or blender.
6. Add the reserved liquid together with the garlic, tahini and the remainder of the lemon juice and olive oil and blend these together at a low speed.
7. Taste and add more salt substitute and black pepper if necessary.
8. Spoon the Hummus into a bowl, cover with a thin layer of olive oil (to prevent it from drying out) and place in the refrigerator.

9. Initially the mixture may appear somewhat runny. How runny it is will vary depending on the quality of the chickpeas (garbanzos) used and is somewhat unpredictable. The Hummus will thicken as it cools.

* Tahini is sesame seed paste.

TZATZICKI

This yogurt-based dip is one of the few recipes in this book to include dairy products. As explained in Chapter 3, every now and then we have included a recipe which contains one of the apparently 'undesirable' foods for arthritis. If you are not actually allergic to dairy products, we suggested that you enjoy the experience of this wonderful Tzatzicki every now and then.

Serves 6 to 8 as a starter

Metric/Imperial		*American*
455g/1lb	Greek yogurt	2 cups
285g/10oz	cucumber, grated	1½ cups
to taste	salt substitute	to taste
2 tbsp	cider vinegar	2 tbsp
4–10	garlic cloves, crushed	4–10
4 tbsp	virgin olive oil	4 tbsp
6 twists	freshly ground black pepper	6 twists
6	black olives, to garnish, optional	6
¼	cucumber, thinly sliced, to garnish, optional	¼

1. Place the yogurt in a bowl.
2. Peel the cucumber, then cut it in half lengthwise and scoop out all the seeds.
3. Coarsely grate the prepared cucumber into a colander to allow the juice to drain away.

4. Add the salt to taste and the cider vinegar and allow to stand for 5 minutes. Then, squeeze any remaining liquid out of the cucumber with your hands. Place the cucumber in the bowl with the yogurt.
5. Add the crushed garlic (use more or fewer cloves according to personal taste), then add the rest of the ingredients, except the garnishes, and stir *thoroughly*. Cover the bowl and place it in the refrigerator for at least 1 hour before serving.
6. To serve, garnish the Tzatziki with the olives and cucumber slices, if desired.

WALNUT AND GARLIC DIP

This attractive dip is an ideal relish with a savoury meal (Lentil and Nut Roast, for example, page 114) or with a salad of carrot, cucumber or celery sticks or with radishes.

Serves 2 as a side dish

Metric/Imperial		*American*
10	garlic cloves, peeled and crushed	10
165g/6oz	wholemeal/wholewheat bread, soaked in water and squeezed so damp	6oz
to taste	salt substitute	to taste
285ml/10fl oz	olive/vegetable oil	1¼ cups
85g/3oz	walnuts or almonds, ground	1 cup
90ml/3fl oz	cider vinegar	⅓ cup

1. Place the crushed garlic in a mixing bowl with the moist breadcrumbs.
2. Add salt substitute to taste and mix well.
3. In another bowl, mix together – adding a little of each at a time – the bread mixture, the oil, ground nuts and cider vinegar. If the mixture becomes too thick (it should have a paste-like texture) add a little warm water.

9

Soups

VEGETABLE BROTH

This mineral- and vitamin-rich soup derives its goodness from the vegetables cooked in it, which are then discarded, leaving behind the broth – the cooking liquid, essentially. This is a very useful recipe as it can be used as you would a stock in other recipes as well as being a highly nourishing thin soup. It also freezes very well.

Serves 4

Metric/Imperial		*American*
2	carrots, unpeeled and scrubbed	2
225g/8oz	potatoes, unpeeled and scrubbed	8oz
1	onion, quartered	1
2	large leeks, cleaned and sliced	2
3	celery sticks, cleaned, destringed and sliced	3

30g/1oz	mushrooms, sliced	1½cups
6	garlic cloves, peeled and left whole	6
2 litres/3¼ pints	water	2½ quarts
1	bay leaf	1
¼ tsp	dried thyme	¼ tsp
4 sprigs	parsley	4 sprigs
5 twists	freshly ground black pepper	5 twists
to taste	salt substitute	to taste

1. Chop the carrots, potatoes and the other vegetables, except the garlic, into large chunks and place in a large saucepan with the water and remaining ingredients and simmer, uncovered, for approximately 1 hour.
2. Remove the pan from the heat and allow to stand for 15 minutes. Then, strain the liquid from the vegetables, discarding the vegetables.
3. Keep the soup refrigerated if it is to be used within days or freeze it for future use as a thin soup or stock.

Note to Cooks

When serving this soup as a drink, a squeeze of lemon juice added to the cup before drinking will bring out the flavours.

GARLIC BROTH

This is ideal as a thin soup served with toast and an excellent alternative to Vegetable Broth (page 80) when you need a stock and want a garlic flavour

Metric/Imperial		*American*
3	garlic heads	3
2	bay leaves	2
2 sprigs	parsley	2 sprigs
¼ tsp	dried thyme	¼ tsp
to taste	salt substitute	to taste
2 litres/3¼ pints	water	2½ quarts

1. Remove all the cloves from the heads of garlic, peel the cloves and cut each one in half.
2. Place these and the remaining ingredients in a saucepan with the water, bring to the boil and allow to simmer for 50 minutes.
3. Remove from the heat and allow to stand for 15 minutes.
4. Strain and discard the garlic cloves and herbs ingredients.
5. Refrigerate the broth if it is to be used within a few days or freeze it for future use as a thin, garlicky soup or flavoured stock for other recipes.

COUNTRYSIDE VEGETABLE SOUP

This soup freezes well so the fact that the quantities given provide up to eight servings makes it an economical and convenient soup to have to hand to use at any time. Serve it with wholemeal (wholewheat) toast, goat's cheese and black olives, to complement the taste, or just enjoy the soup on its own.

Serves 6 to 8 as a main meal

Metric/Imperial		*American*
255g/9oz	cabbage, shredded	2 cups
2	artichokes (page 35)	2
225g/8oz	celery sticks, plus leaves, chopped	1½ cups
255g/9oz	mushrooms, washed and chopped	3½cups
115g/4oz	onion, chopped	1 cup
170g/6oz	French/fine green beans, chopped	6 oz
115g/4oz	fresh spinach, shredded	2 cups
140g/5oz	carrots, chopped	1 cup
255g/9oz	fennel bulb, chopped	2 cups
115g/4oz	courgette/zucchini, chopped	2 cups
2 litres/ 3¼ pints	water or Vegetable Broth (page 80)	2½quarts
240ml/8fl oz	olive/vegetable oil	1 cup
to taste	salt substitute	to taste
5 twists	freshly ground black pepper	5 twists

1. Place all the ingredients, apart from the oil, salt substitute and pepper, in a large saucepan, then stir in the oil, salt and pepper.
2. Bring to the boil and allow to simmer, covered, for 1 hour, at which time check the ingredients for tenderness. Tastes differ and if you like them more tender than they are at this point continue to simmer until the desired texture is achieved.
3. Freeze what is not used in serving-sized containers for convenient and quick future meals.

Notes to Cooks

The addition of a small amount of pasta to the simmering soup 15 minutes before the desired tenderness of the vegetables is achieved (after it has been simmering for approximately 50 minutes) makes a tasty and filling variation. Short-cut macaroni, spaghetti broken into short pieces or other suitable pasta (shells, for example) may be added if the soup is not going to be subsequently frozen.

If previously frozen soup is being prepared, the pasta can be added when you reheat it. Allow approximately 30g (1oz/½ cup) per serving and simmer for about 15 minutes. If you prefer a smoother texture, put the soup through a blender.

CLASSIC LENTIL SOUP

Along with nut roasts, lentil soup remains a predictable butt of many anti-vegetarian jokes. It is, however, one of the most nourishing dishes of all and can be absolutely delicious. It has the added bonus of being easy to prepare and freezing well, making it a convenient and economical meal.

Serve this soup with wholemeal (wholewheat) toast for a complete protein meal. By combining a pulse (legume – the lentils) with a grain, all the essential amino acids are supplied, making the eating of animal protein unnecessary.

Serves 4 as a main meal

Metric/Imperial		*American*
350g/12oz	brown lentils	1¾ cups
1.8 litres/ 3 pints	water or Vegetable Broth or Garlic Broth (pages 80 and 82)	1½ quarts
140g/5oz	medium carrots, chopped	1 cup
115g/4oz	celery sticks, chopped	1 cup
10	garlic cloves, peeled	10
1 tbsp	dried oregano	1 tbsp
240ml/8fl oz	olive/vegetable oil	1 cup
1 tbsp	cider vinegar, optional	1 tbsp

1. Pick over the lentils, removing any grit and little stones and wash well.
2. Place in a saucepan with the water or broth. Bring to the boil and allow to simmer for approximately 30 minutes, at which time, skim any froth from the surface and discard it.
3. Add all the remaining ingredients, apart from the cider vinegar. Add a little more boiling water if the consistency appears overly thick.
4. Allow to simmer over a gentle heat until the lentils and vegetables are tender (approximately 45 to 60 minutes more). The texture of the soup should then be thick.
5. Remove the pan from the heat, add the cider vinegar and mix it in well.
6. Any surplus soup can be frozen for convenient use later, or prepare double the quantity and freeze.

BEAN SOUP

This is one of the most nourishing and easy soups we know. You can make either a 'with tomato' or 'tomato-free' version if you wish to avoid the nightshade family.

Serve as a main meal with wholemeal (wholewheat) or rye toast (use olive oil rather than butter on this if you do not want to eat it plain.

Serves 1 to 2

Metric/Imperial		*American*
200g/7oz	haricot/navy beans	1 cup
115g/4oz	celery, chopped	1 cup
140g/5oz	carrots, chopped	⅔ cup
55g/2oz	onion, chopped	½ cup
210ml/7½fl oz	olive/vegetable oil	1 cup
pinch	paprika	pinch
6 twists	freshly ground black pepper	6 twists
to taste	salt substitute, optional	to taste
2	medium tomatoes or	2
1 tbsp	tomato purée/paste, optional	1 tbsp
85g/3oz	rice flakes or couscous, to thicken, if necessary	½ cup

1. Soak the beans overnight.
2. The next day, discard the water, then rinse the beans well.
3. Place the beans in a saucepan with 3 inches of water and bring to boil, removing the froth that forms. Allow to simmer until tender (30 to 90 minutes, depending on the quality of the beans and the hardness of the water).
4. When the beans are tender, discard the water, rinse out the pan, then return the beans to the pan and cover them with boiling water. Add all the remaining ingredients.
5. Bring to boil and simmer for 1 hour, adding more water if it becomes thick during cooking.
6. If, five to ten minutes before the end of the hour, the soup is still somewhat runny, it can be thickened by adding the rice flakes or couscous.

Note for Cooks

To have home-made convenience food ready for when you have no time to cook, make double the recipe as this soup freezes very well.

10

Side Dishes

CELERIAC AND CARROTS WITH GINGER

Please note that this dish contains a very small amount of tomato, one of the 'forbidden' *Solenaceae* family, in the form of purée. It is suggested that these foods are eaten no more than once in five days by people with arthritis.

The nutritional value of celeriac (celery root) is similar to that of celery and so it is recommended for people with arthritic conditions.

Serves 3

Metric/Imperial		*American*
425g/15oz	celeriac/celery root, peeled and diced	3 cups
425g/15oz	carrots, diced	3 cups
60ml/2fl oz	lemon juice	¼ cup
30ml/1fl oz	puréed ginger*	⅛ cup
30ml/1fl oz	tomato purée/paste	⅛ cup
170g/6oz	onion, peeled and chopped	1 cup
210ml/7½oz	olive/vegetable oil	¾ cup
425ml/15fl oz	water	2 cups

1. Place all the ingredients, including the water, in a saucepan.
2. Bring to the boil and allow to simmer until all the water has evaporated, ensuring that the ingredients do not stick to the pan when this happens by shaking the pan gently from time to time. Serve while warm or at room temperature.

* Available at all good supermarkets.

BAKED HEAD OF GARLIC, CHICAGO STYLE

A whole head of garlic, baked, is a delight if eaten as a side dish or if the buttery contents are spread on bread or toast.

Serves 1 to 2

Metric/Imperial		*American*
1	garlic head, whole	1
2 tbsp	virgin olive oil	2 tbsp
pinch	fresh or dried oregano	pinch

1. Preheat the oven to 180°C/350°F/gas mark 4.
2. Place the head of garlic on a piece of kitchen (aluminium) foil large enough to wrap it.
3. Pour the oil over the garlic, then sprinkle the oregano over the top and wrap the garlic up completely.
4. Bake the garlic in the preheated oven for 10 to 15 minutes.
5. Remove from oven, unwrap the garlic and break off the individual cloves. Squeeze the cloves and spread the contents on bread, toast or eat on its own.

Alternative Barbecue Method

1. The head of garlic can be put straight onto the hot coals of a barbecue or living room fire and allowed to brown. The coals should be hot and glowing, but there should be no actual flames.

2. Once removed from the coals, the outside may appear burned and hard but the inner flesh will be soft and just right for eating.

STUFFED ONIONS

This side dish complements all fish dishes.

Serves 3 to 4

Metric/Imperial		*American*
4	medium to large onions	4
1 tbsp	sultanas/golden seedless raisins	1 tbsp
1 tbsp	pine nuts	1 tbsp
1 tbsp	cider vinegar	1 tbsp
1 tsp	oregano	1 tsp
3 twists (per onion)	freshly ground black pepper	3 twists (per onion)
to taste	salt substitute	to taste
90ml/3fl oz	olive/vegetable oil	generous ¼ cup

1. Preheat the oven to 180°C/350°F/gas mark 4.
2. Peel the onions and, using a grapefruit knife, remove a central core from the onion that is approximately 1½ cm (¾ in) wide, leaving the bottom intact.
3. Chop the part of the onion you have removed finely and place in a bowl with all the remaining ingredients, except the salt and pepper and reserving 60ml (2fl oz/¼ cup) of the oil.
4. Mix the ingredients in the bowl and stuff these into the hollowed out onions.

5. Place the stuffed onions in a small heatproof baking dish, then pour over the reserved oil and season with salt substitute to taste and black pepper.
6. Pour 240ml (8fl oz/1cup) of water around the onions and bake in the preheated oven until all water has evaporated, about 50 minutes.

COURGETTES (ZUCCHINI) WITH CARROTS AND GINGER

Serve as a side dish with any savoury meal.

Serves 2

Metric/Imperial		*American*
455g/1lb	courgettes/zucchini, washed	1lb
285g/10oz	large carrots, scrubbed	10oz
225g/8oz	onion	8oz
2 tbsp	grated fresh root ginger	2 tbsp
or		
1 tbsp	ginger purée/paste	1 tbsp
200ml/7fl oz	olive/vegetable oil	¾ cup
pinch	paprika	pinch
5 twists	freshly ground black pepper	5 twists
to taste	salt substitute	to taste

1. Cut each of the courgettes (zucchini) into 3 or 4 chunks.
2. Cut the carrots into 3 or 4 chunks.
3. Cut the onion into quarters.
4. Place the prepared vegetables and all the remaining ingredients in a saucepan and just cover with cold water.
5. Bring to the boil, then cook over a medium heat, simmering, until all the water has evaporated, stirring from time to time.

ALKMINI'S DAIRY-FREE SANDWICH

Butter is fat-rich and promotes inflammation (see Chapter 1), while margarine and other butter substitutes contain strangely engineered fats that make them undesirable if you are trying to eat a healthier diet.

So, what can you do? Next time you make a sandwich try using olive oil instead. If you have never tried it, then you are in for a pleasant surprise. This new taste experience will be enhanced if you make sure you use a good-quality oil – one that says that it is virgin and a first, cold-pressed oil.

If you like dairy foods and are not sensitive or allergic to them, you can use virtually fat-free fromage frais (fromage blanc) and cottage cheese as well as other very low-fat cheeses. If you wish to include these in your sandwich, they make it even tastier.

For those who are wheat sensitive, use pure rye bread.

For those who are yeast sensitive, use sourdough, unyeasted bread.

For those who are grain sensitive, use soya or corn bread.

Serves 1

Metric/Imperial		*American*
2 slices	wholemeal/wholewheat or rye bread or one of the options given above	2 slices
2 tsp	olive oil	2 tsp
2	slices of onion	2
2 leaves	rocket/arugula	2 leaves
or		
2 sprigs	watercress	2 sprigs
4	large, halved, stoned/ depipped olives	4
1½ tsp	virtually fat-free fromage frais/fromage blanc or cottage cheese, optional (see above)	1½ tsp

1. With a pastry brush, paint the oil over one surface of each slice of bread.
2. Onto one slice, on the oiled side, place the onion slices, the rocket (arugula) leaves or sprigs of watercress and the of olive halves.
3. Place the other slice on top of this, oiled side inwards, and press together. If you are using fromage frais (fromage blanc) or cottage cheese, spread it on this second slice before pressing it on to the first slice of bread. Cut the sandwich in two and eat, taking care to have an absorbent serviette available to wipe your hand if you have been too generous with the olive oil.

BEAN STEW

Serve as a side dish with any of the savoury main courses in this book.

Serves 3 or 4

Metric/Imperial		*American*
425g/15oz	French/fine green beans	15oz
115g/4oz	onions, chopped	1 cup
120ml/4fl oz	olive oil	½ cup
170g/6oz	young, tender carrots, chopped	1 cup
30g/1oz	fresh parsley, chopped	1 cup
1 tsp	brown sugar	1 tsp
1 tsp	ginger purée/paste	1 tsp
5 twists	freshly ground black pepper	5 twists
to taste	salt substitute	to taste
240ml/8fl oz	water	1 cup

1. Trim the beans.
2. Place the onions in a saucepan with the oil and cook until the onions have softened but not browned.
3. Add the beans, carrots, parsley, sugar, ginger purée (paste), pepper, salt substitute and the water, cover and simmer until the liquid has virtually all evaporated, about 50 minutes.

Variations

Tofu is a nutritious addition to this stew. Dice 185g (6½oz/¾ cup) of tofu and add it to the stew about 5 minutes before all the water has evaporated to transform this side dish into a main meal. Tofu has little intrinsic taste but acquires that of foods with which it is cooked. It also requires very little cooking so can be added to any dish towards the end of the cooking time.

You can replace the beans with leeks. Then, omit the parsley and you can add 1½ cups preboiled rice and/or tofu to the stew towards the end of cooking.

MUSHROOMS WITH GARLIC AND GINGER

There are few more delicious combinations than this and, as is the aim of all the recipes in this book, it is good for you, too!

Serve hot or at room temperature as an accompaniment to any savoury dish.

Serves 2

Metric/Imperial		*American*
225g/8oz	button mushrooms	4 cups
115g/4oz	onion, sliced or grated	1 cup
285g/10oz	carrots, sliced	2 cups
8	garlic cloves, chopped	8
55g/2oz	ginger purée/paste	⅓ cup
240ml/8fl oz	olive/vegetable oil	1 cup
pinch	cayenne pepper	pinch
4 twists	freshly ground black pepper	4 twists
120ml/4fl oz	water	½ cup
to taste	salt substitute	to taste

1. Wipe the mushrooms, cut them in half and place in a shallow saucepan.
2. Add all the other ingredients and heat gently, uncovered, until the contents are sizzling. Stir to mix the ingredients together well. Then, lower the heat, cover and allow to simmer gently, stirring from time to time, until all the water has evaporated (about 25 minutes).

COUSCOUS WITH ALMONDS AND PINE NUTS

Couscous is a wheat product that is precooked and therefore requires very little additional preparation. It is much used in Middle Eastern cooking and quite delicious. However, if you are sensitive to wheat, try another recipe.

Serves 2 to 3

Metric/Imperial		*American*
170g/6oz	couscous	1 cup
210ml/7½fl oz	boiling water	1 cup
to taste	salt substitute	to taste
4 twists	freshly ground black pepper	4 twists
2 tbsp	olive oil	2 tbsp
85g/3oz	fennel bulb, chopped	½ cup
115g/4oz	apple, diced	½ cup
55g/2oz	pine nuts	⅓ cup
55g/2oz	flaked/slivered almonds, to garnish	⅓ cup

1. Place the couscous in a heatproof bowl and pour the boiling water onto it and add the salt substitute. Cover and allow to stand for 10 minutes.
2. Uncover and stir in the olive oil and pepper, then add the rest of the ingredients, except the almonds, and mix thoroughly.
3. Spoon onto serving plates and garnish with the almonds before serving.

Note to Cooks

The apple can be replaced with pineapple for an exotic alternative taste.

SWEET POTATOES WITH MUSHROOMS

Potatoes are members of the *Solanaceae* (nightshade) family, which, in large quantities, are undesirable if you have arthritis. Sweet potatoes contain far less of the substances that cause the problems than do ordinary potatoes. Sweet potatoes also contain very useful levels of vitamins (such as A and C) and minerals, such as potassium. There are different varieties of sweet potato and you should seek out those with white (rather than yellowish) flesh and a purple (rather than brown/beige) tinge to their skins because of their texture.

Serve with any savoury meal or with a salad.

Serves 3

Metric/Imperial		*American*
680g/1½lb	sweet potatoes	1½lb
115g/4oz	shiitaki mushrooms	2 cups
210ml/7½fl oz	olive/vegetable oil	1 cup
1 tbsp	thyme or oregano	1 tbsp
5 twists	freshly ground black pepper	5 twists
to taste	salt substitute	to taste
210ml/7½fl oz	water	1 cup

1. Preheat the oven to 200°C/400°F/gas mark 6.
2. Peel the sweet potatoes, then cut them in half lengthwise and each half into 3 pieces.
3. Wipe the mushrooms and discard the stalks. Place them, with the sweet potato pieces, in an ovenproof dish.

4. Add all the remaining ingredients, mix well, then add the water.
5. Cover the container with kitchen (aluminum) foil and bake in the preheated oven for 30 minutes. Remove the foil, turn the potatoes and return to the oven to bake until all the water has evaporated and the sweet potatoes are tender (20 and 30 minutes).

11

Vegetarian Main Courses

SAVOURY PUMPKIN PIE

Dairy products are often considered undesirable foods for people with arthritis (see Chapter 2) – usually because of the high fat content and the influence this has on inflammation and sometimes because people have a sensitivity to dairy foods. If there is no actual sensitivity, then, just as with tomatoes, you can have dairy products from time to time and then the influence on inflammation will be minimal. It is possible to substitute tofu (soya bean curd) for the feta but the results are not as delicious.

Serves 6

Metric/Imperial		*American*
900g/2lb	pumpkin, peeled, depipped and coarsely grated	2lb
1½ tsp	salt substitute	1½ tsp

455g/1lb	feta cheese, grated	2 cups
210ml/7½fl oz	soya milk	1 cup
140g/5oz	rice flakes	1½ cups
85g/3oz	flaked/slivered almonds	1 cup
70g/2½ oz	pine nuts	½ cup
115g/4oz	onion, grated	1 cup
30g/1oz	fresh parsley, chopped	1 cup
4	egg whites	4
1 packet	filo pastry, defrosted	1 packet
120ml/4fl oz	olive/vegetable oil	½ cup

1. Preheat the oven to 170°C/325°F/gas mark 3.
2. Place the grated pumpkin in a colander and add the salt substitute, mix well and allow to drain for 2 hours.
3. Squeeze the pumpkin with your hands to extract all the surplus liquid.
4. Place the drained pumpkin in a bowl and add all the remaining ingredients, except the egg whites, filo pastry and oil. Mix well.
5. Beat the egg whites well and fold them into the pumpkin mixture.
6. Line a large square or rectangular ovenproof baking dish with 3 layers of filo pastry, brushing oil over each layer.
7. Spoon the pumpkin mixture into the lined dish, levelling the top with the back of a spoon.
8. Lay a layer of filo pastry over the top of the pie, brush with oil and top with another 2 layers of pastry, brushing each layer, including the top, with oil.

9. With a sharp knife, score the top of the pie with a grid to mark the 6 portions.
10. Bake in the preheated oven until the surface is golden brown (approximately 50 minutes).
11. Serve hot or cold.

COURGETTE (ZUCCHINI) CAKES OR LOAF WITH ALMONDS

Serve with salad or cooked vegetables.

Serves 4 to 6

Metric/Imperial		*American*
225g/8oz	courgettes/zucchini, coarsely grated	2 cups
115g/4oz	onion, coarsely grated	1 cup
170g/6oz	carrots, coarsely grated	1½ cups
30g/1oz	fresh parsley, chopped	½ cup
30g/1oz	fresh dill, chopped	½ cup
45g/1½oz plus 1 tbsp	flaked/slivered almonds, to garnish if making a loaf	½ cup plus 1 tbsp
85g/3oz	ground almonds	1 cup
3	egg whites	3
5 twists	freshly ground black pepper	5 twists
pinch	cayenne pepper	pinch
to taste	salt substitute	to taste
140ml/5fl oz	olive/vegetable oil	generous ½ cup

1. Place the grated courgettes (zucchini), onion and carrots in a bowl.
2. Add the parsley, dill both kinds of almonds and mix well.
3. Lightly beat the egg whites into the mixture and add the black pepper, cayenne, salt substitute and 2 tablespoons of the oil. Mix thoroughly with a wooden spoon.

4. *To make little cakes*, pour the rest of the oil into a frying pan and heat until it shows signs of 'steaming' at which time, using a large spoon, take sufficient of the mixture to form into individual cakes and place these, one at a time, in the hot oil. Reduce the temperature whilst frying.
5. Repeat this process until the pan is full and, with the help of another spoon, turn the cakes one at a time until they are golden brown on both sides. Drain on kitchen paper.
6. Continue until all the mixture has been used, adding more oil if necessary.
7. *To make a loaf*, preheat the oven to 190°C/375°F/gas mark 5. Oil a 455-g (1-lb) loaf tin, pile the courgette (zucchini) mixture into it, sprinkle the extra flaked (slivered) almonds over the top (cover with foil for the first 20 minutes to avoid burning the almonds) and bake in the preheated oven for about 45 minutes, until the top is turning golden brown. Turn out of the tin and slice. The loaf can be served hot or cold.

PASTA WITH OLIVES AND GARLIC

By adding olive/vegetable oil, even more garlic and stoned (depipped) olives to the cooked spaghetti before the sauce is added to the dish, an even richer eating experience is guaranteed.

A number of pastas are now available that are wheat-free if you are sensitive to wheat. Rice, corn, soya and other wheat-free spaghetti is widely available from healthfood shops and specialist food suppliers.

Serves 3

Metric/Imperial		*American*
1½ litres/ 2½ pints	water or Vegetable or Garlic Broth (pages 80–82)	2½ quarts
2 tsp	salt substitute	2 tsp
455g/1lb	wholemeal/wholewheat or rice spaghetti	1lb
680g/1½lb	Mushroom Sauce (page 40)	3 to 4 cups
120ml/4fl oz	olive/vegetable oil	½ cup
4	garlic cloves, crushed	4
8	large black olives, stoned (depipped) and quartered	8
4 twists	freshly ground black pepper	4 twists
30g/1oz	hard cheese of your choice, grated, optional	½ cup

1. Pour the water or broth into a saucepan and add the salt substitute. Bring to the boil, then add the spaghetti and stir periodically, cooking until it is tender (approximately 15 minutes).
2. Remove the pan from the heat and drain off the cooking water or stock.
3. Meanwhile, gently warm the Mushroom Sauce.
4. Rinse out the saucepan you cooked the spaghetti in, return the spaghetti to the pan and add the olive/vegetable oil, garlic, olives, pepper and half the Mushroom Sauce and mix together gently but thoroughly.
5. Serve on platter, pouring over the remainder of the warmed Mushroom Sauce.
6. Sprinkle the grated cheese over the top, unless you are following a dairy-free diet, of course.

BUTTER BEAN ROAST

This is a traditional Mediterranean peasant meal. It contains tinned tomatoes and it is suggested that tomatoes should not be eaten more than once or twice a week by anyone with an arthritic condition, so go ahead and enjoy this dish if you are within this allowance!

As with many bean dishes, you need to soak the beans overnight. Note too that changing the water after partially cooking the beans the next day helps avoid the usual unwanted side-effect of eating beans – gassiness.

Serves 4 to 5

Metric/Imperial		*American*
455g/1lb	dried butter/lima beans	2½ cups
340ml/12fl oz	olive/vegetable oil	1½ cups
30g/1oz	fresh parsley, chopped	1 cup
455g/1lb	tinned tomatoes	2⅔ cups
6	garlic cloves, halved	6
120g/4oz	celery sticks, including leaves, sliced	1 cup
120g/4oz	onion, raw, diced	1 cup
120g/4oz	carrots, chopped	1 cup
¼ tsp	paprika	¼ tsp
6 twists	freshly ground black pepper	6 twists
to taste	salt substitute	to taste
¼ tsp	cayenne	¼ tsp

1. Soak the beans overnight.
2. The next day, drain off the soaking water, rinse the beans, then place them in a saucepan with water to cover. Bring to the boil and then simmer for 30 minutes.
3. Drain off the beans' cooking water and pour in the fresh boiling water. Simmer for a further 30 minutes.
4. Towards the end of this time, boil some more water in a kettle or another saucepan and set the oven to 350°F/180°C/gas mark 4.
5. Drain the beans and place in a deep ovenproof baking dish, together with the remaining ingredients, mixing them all together.
6. Pour in enough boiling water to cover.
7. Cover the container with kitchen (aluminum) foil and bake in the preheated oven for 30 minutes.
8. Remove the foil and return to the oven to bake until all the water has evaporated and the beans are tender with some on the top browning or crisping a little. Exactly how long this will take will depend on the quality of the beans and the hardness of the water, about 30 to 60 minutes.

LENTIL AND NUT ROAST

This savoury meal is a complete protein combination that can be substituted for animal protein, containing as it does pulses (legumes – the lentils), nuts and grains (breadcrumbs). You will note that egg whites are used in this recipe rather than whole eggs and this is in line with the suggestion by the famous Dr Colin Dong in his book *New Hope for the Arthritic* (Hart-Davis MacGibbon, 1976) mentioned earlier that egg yolks are often an irritant for those with arthritis. The whites are used as a means of binding together what would otherwise be a crumbly mixture.

You can substitute ginger for the tomato purée (paste) and this is delicious.

This dish would be well complemented by a side salad, such as the Middle Eastern Celery Salad (page 59) or Mixed Vegetable Cooked Salad (see page 69), and/or the Walnut and Garlic Dip (page 79) as a relish.

Serves 6 to 8

Metric/Imperial		*American*
225g/8oz	lentils	1 cup
115g/4oz	onion, chopped	1 cup
8	garlic cloves, whole, peeled	8
2 tbsp	olive/vegetable oil	2 tbsp

170g/6oz	ground walnuts or almonds and/or pine nuts	1 cup
170g/6oz	fresh wholemeal/ wholewheat breadcrumbs	3 cups
2 tbsp	tomato or ginger purée/paste	2 tbsp
1½ tsp	dried oregano	1½ tsp
30g/1oz	fresh parsley, chopped	1 cup
2	egg whites, beaten	2
5 twists	freshly ground black pepper	5 twists
to taste	salt substitute	to taste
5 sprigs	fresh parsley, to garnish, optional	5 sprigs
3 or 4 slices	onion, separated into rings to garnish, optional	3 or 4 slices

1. Soak the lentils for 2 hours, then drain off the water and wash well.
2. Place the lentils in a saucepan, covering with fresh water and bring to the boil. Simmer for 20 minutes, then remove the pan from the heat and drain off any remaining cooking water.
3. In a large saucepan, lightly fry the onion and the garlic cloves in the oil.
4. Remove the pan from the heat and add the nuts, lentils, breadcrumbs, tomato or ginger purée (paste), oregano, parsley and egg whites.
5. Preheat the oven to 180°C/350°F/gas mark 4.
6. Season with pepper and salt substitute and pile the mixture into an oiled 455-g (1-lb) loaf tin lined with

kitchen (aluminium) foil, the foil having also been oiled. Smooth the top with the back of a spoon and bake the loaf in the preheated oven for 1 hour.

7. When it is done, leave the loaf in the tin to cool for 20 minutes. Then, run a knife around the edges and turn out the loaf. Place on a serving platter and garnish with the sprigs of parsley and onion rings, if using. Serve hot or cold.

MUSHROOM AND NUT ROAST

As with the Lentil and Nut Roast (page 114), the nuts and grains (breadcrumbs) in this dish provide complete protein, making it an excellent substitute for an animal protein meal. Also, just the egg whites are used rather than whole eggs as some experts believe that egg yolks can act as an irritant in arthritis. The egg whites bind the mixture together very effectively.

Walnut and Garlic Dip (page 79) served as a condiment for the roast plus a crunchy side salad would make for an excellent combination of tastes and textures, or else try it with the Mixed Vegetable Cooked Salad (page 69).

Serves 6 to 8

Metric/Imperial		*American*
45g/1½oz	ground walnuts	½ cup
45g/1½oz	ground almonds	½ cup
45g/1½oz	ground cashew nuts	½ cup
45g/1½oz	flaked/slivered almonds	½ cup
45g/1½oz	pine nuts	½ cup
170g/6oz	fresh wholemeal/ wholewheat breadcrumbs	3 cups
115g/4oz	onion, chopped	1 cup
115g/4oz	button mushrooms, finely chopped	1 cup
225ml/7½fl oz	olive/vegetable oil	1 cup
8	garlic cloves, whole, peeled	8
2 tbsp	ginger purée/paste	2 tbsp
1½ tsp	dried oregano	1½ tsp

15g/½oz	fresh parsley, chopped	½ cup
5 twists	freshly ground black pepper	5 twists
to taste	salt substitute	to taste
2	egg whites, beaten	2
5 sprigs	parsley, to garnish, optional	5 sprigs
1	medium onion, sliced and separated into rings, to garnish, optional	1

1. In a large bowl, mix together the nuts and bread-crumbs.
2. In a large saucepan, lightly fry the onion and mush-rooms in the oil. When these have softened but before the onion has browned, add the garlic cloves and cook for a minute or so.
3. Remove the pan from the heat and add the ginger purée (paste), herbs and seasoning. Add this mixture to the nuts and breadcrumbs in the large bowl.
4. Mix this well until it takes on a smooth texture then add the egg whites.
5. Preheat the oven to 180°C/350°F/gas mark 4.
6. Pile the mixture into an oiled 455-g (1-lb) loaf tin lined with kitchen (aluminium) foil, the foil having also been oiled. Smooth the top with the back of a spoon and cover with a piece of oiled foil. Bake in the preheated oven for approximately 1 hour.
7. Leave the loaf in the tin to cool for 20 minutes, then run a knife around the edges before turning it out.
8. Garnish with the sprigs of parsley and onion rings, if using, and serve, sliced, hot or cold.

SPINACH AND RICE WITH DILL AND GARLIC

Serves 3 to 4

Metric/Imperial		*American*
115g/4oz	onion, chopped	1 cup
240ml/8fl oz	olive/vegetable oil	1 cup
900g/2lb	fresh spinach, well washed and cut into large pieces	2lb
450ml/15fl oz	warm water	2 cups
200g/7 oz	brown rice	1 cup
4	garlic cloves, sliced	4
60g/2oz	spring onions/scallions, sliced	½ cup
30g/1oz	fresh dill, chopped	1 cup
30g/1oz	fresh parsley, chopped	1 cup
6 twists	freshly ground black pepper	6 twists
to taste	salt substitute	to taste
2 tbsp	lemon juice	2 tbsp

1. Place the onion in a large saucepan with the oil and sauté until the onion is soft but not brown, then add the spinach.
2. Stir until all the spinach is lightly cooked, at which time add the water, rice, garlic, spring onions (scallions), dill, parsley, salt substitute and pepper.
3. Allow to simmer for approximately 45 minutes semi-covered, stirring periodically, until all the water has evaporated.

4. Test the rice to assess whether or not it is adequately cooked. If it is not, add a little more warm water and continue to simmer until the rice is soft.
5. When almost all the water has evaporated or when serving, add the lemon juice – it enhances the flavour.

LEEK AND RICE STEW

Serves 2

Metric/Imperial		*American*
565g/1¼lb	leeks	1¼lb
200g/7oz	brown rice, soaked overnight	1 cup
60ml/2fl oz	olive/vegetable oil	¼ cup
115g/4oz	onion, chopped	1 cup
5 twists	freshly ground black pepper	5 twists
to taste	salt substitute	to taste

1. Clean the leeks and chop them into 4-cm (1½-in) lengths.
2. Place these, together with the remaining ingredients, in a saucepan and cover (only just) with water or Vegetable Broth (page 80).
3. Heat gently, without boiling, so that the contents simmer until all the liquid has evaporated. Serve hot or cold.

SPAGHETTI WITH PEAS

This unusual pasta dish has the advantage of containing no dairy products, unless you choose to sprinkle some grated cheese over the finished dish, and no tomatoes or meat.

A number of pastas are now available that are wheat-free if you like pasta but are sensitive to wheat. Rice, corn, soya and other wheat-free pastas can be found at healthfood shops and specialist food suppliers.

Serves 3 to 4

Metric/Imperial		*American*
200ml/7fl oz	olive/vegetable oil	¾ cup
115g/4oz	onion, chopped	1 cup
115g/4oz	celery sticks, chopped	1 cup
3	garlic cloves, chopped	3
15g/½oz	fresh parsley, chopped	½ cup
340g/12oz	fresh peas, shelled and washed	2 cups
6 twists	freshly ground black pepper	6 twists
to taste	salt substitute	to taste
240ml/8fl oz	water	1 cup
455g/16oz	wholemeal/wholewheat spaghetti or other pasta	1lb
3 twists	freshly ground black pepper	3 twists
30g/1oz	hard cheese, grated, to garnish, optional	½ cup

1. Warm the oil in a saucepan over a medium heat and add the onion, celery, garlic and parsley. Stir constantly until the vegetables are tender.
2. Add the peas, half the number of twists of pepper, the salt substitute and the water. Allow to simmer until the water has evaporated.
3. Meanwhile, bring a pan of water with a pinch of salt substitute added to it to the boil. Break the spaghetti into thirds and throw into the pan. Cook until sufficiently tender, then drain in a colander.
4. Return the spaghetti to its saucepan and season with the 3 twists of pepper and, if using, add the grated cheese and mix well but gently over a low heat before adding the pea mixture. Stir it in and warm it through briefly, then serve immediately.

STUFFED CANNELLONI

This is extremely good served with Middle Eastern Celery Salad (page 59) or Green Peasant Salad and Dressing (page 66).

Serves 3

Metric/Imperial		*American*
1.5litres/ 2½pints	water	1½ quarts
1 quantity	Mushroom Sauce (page 40)	1 quantity
25	cannelloni tubes	25
100g/3½oz	chickpeas/garbanzos, soaked overnight	1 cup
75g/1¼oz	fresh rosemary	¼ cup
to taste	salt substitute	to taste
240ml/8fl oz	olive/vegetable oil	1 cup
5 twists	freshly ground black pepper	5 twists

1. Bring the water to the boil in a large saucepan.
2. When the water is boiling, place the cannelloni tubes in it and cook for 1 minute (unless your cannelloni does not need to be preboiled).
3. Meanwhile, drain off the soaking water from the chickpeas (garbanzos) and wash them well. Place them in a saucepan and add water to cover, the rosemary and salt substitute to taste. Bring to the boil and cook until tender, about 30 to 60 minutes.

4. Drain the chickpeas (garbanzos) and mix them with the Mushroom Sauce. Stuff the cannelloni with this mixture, then lay the stuffed tubes side by side in a large, deep frying pan. It may be necessary to create a second layer of cannelloni on top of the first one.
5. Pour the olive oil on top of the cannelloni, along with any sauce left over from stuffing the tubes. Grind the pepper over the top and pour in only just enough water to cover the entire contents of the pan.
6. Cook over a very low heat, gently shaking the pan from time to time to ensure that the contents do not stick, until all the water has evaporated (approximately 45 minutes).

LEEK PIE WITH TOFU

The traditional Mediterranean leek pie on which this is based includes cottage cheese or feta. However, in this recipe, cheese has been replaced with tofu. It also uses egg whites rather than whole eggs, making this a nutritious dish suitable for anyone with an arthritic condition. Of course, if there is no sensitivity to dairy products, you can use fat-free cottage cheese or feta and whole eggs if you wish or for a change.

Serves 4

Metric/Imperial		*American*
120ml/4fl oz	olive/vegetable oil	½ cup
900g/2lb	medium leeks, cleaned and coarsely chopped	2lb
225g/8oz	tofu	1 cup
2	egg whites	2
2 tbsp	finely ground rye crispbread	2 tbsp
5 twists	freshly ground black pepper	5 twists
to taste	salt substitute	to taste
1 quantity	Shortcrust/Pie Pastry (page 38)	1 quantity

1. Heat the oil in a frying pan and sauté the leeks over a low heat, uncovered, until all the liquid has evaporated.
2. Meanwhile, crumble the tofu and lay it on kitchen paper for 15 minutes to allow the surplus moisture to drain off.
3. When the tofu is ready, beat the egg whites and add the tofu to them.
4. Add the tofu and egg white mixture to the leeks, together with the ground crispbread, pepper and salt substitute, and gently mix together.
5. Preheat the oven to 190°C/375°F/gas mark 5.
6. Roll out the pastry and use it to line an oiled 20-cm (8-in) diameter flan (tart) dish. Pile the leek and tofu mixture into it, smoothing the top with the back of a spoon and then cover with pastry, wetting edges and pressing together to seal. Then, score the surface of the pie (deep enough to allow steam to escape) into portion-size wedges for ease of serving, and bake in the preheated oven until the pastry is golden brown, approximately 50 to 60 minutes.
7. Allow the pie to stand for at least 10 minutes after removing from the oven before cutting it, then serve hot or at room temperature as you prefer.

ARTICHOKE AND HERB STEW

There are few more cleansing vegetables than artichokes, which have been proven to have beneficial effects on liver function. When they are combined with parsley, garlic and onions, the benefits are amplified. This delicious, wholesome and easily made vegetarian dish has roots that stretch back as long ago as early European history.

Serve the stew with olives, wholemeal (wholewheat) bread and Walnut and Garlic Dip (page 79). You can also serve this in smaller quantities as a side dish with any of the fish or poultry recipes in this book.

Serves 3

Metric/Imperial		*American*
4	globe artichokes (page 35)	4
170g/6oz	spring onions/scallions, chopped	1¾cups
60g/2oz	fresh parsley, chopped	2 cups
455g/1lb	fresh or frozen peas	2½ cups
170ml/6fl oz	olive/vegetable oil	⅔ cup
to taste	salt substitute	to taste
6 twists	freshly ground black pepper	6 twists

1. Place the vegetables in a large (non-stick if possible) saucepan and add the oil, salt substitute and pepper and cover with water.
2. Bring to the boil, then simmer until all the water has evaporated. Stir from time to time during the cooking.
3. Serve hot or at room temperature.

STIR-FRIED TOFU WITH GINGER, VEGETABLES AND NUTS

Tofu provides the essential nutrients found in soya beans, most notably protein, and it takes on the flavours of the foods with which it is cooked, so it is good for you and versatile, too. Stir-frying the vegetables in this dish ensures that little of their food value is lost in the cooking and yet, having been cooked, they are more easily digested.

Serve with rice or as an accompaniment to any other savoury dish.

Serves 2

Metric/Imperial		*American*
30g/1oz	cashew or pistachio nuts, shelled	¼cup
2 tbsp	olive or safflower oil	2 tbsp
2	carrots, sliced	2
1	courgette/zucchini, sliced	1
2	celery sticks/stalks, sliced	2
3	spring onions/scallions, chopped	3
115g/4oz	mushrooms, whole or sliced	1 cup
115g/4oz	mangetout/snowpeas	1 cup
115g/4oz	tofu, cubed or sliced	½ cup
1 tbsp	grated root ginger	1 tbsp

1. Place the nuts into either a wok or deep frying pan and dry roast these for a few minutes until they turn golden. Agitate the pan or use a wooden spoon or spatula to stir-fry them to prevent them burning.
2. Remove the nuts and place them on a plate to cool.
3. Very lightly oil the pan using half the oil and stir-fry the carrots for a minute or 2 before adding the rest of the vegetables, the tofu and oil, but not the ginger.
4. Keep shaking the pan or use a wooden spatula or spoon to stir the ingredients as they cook for a further minute or 2.
5. Add the ginger and nuts and cook for a further 30 seconds before turning out the contents into a serving bowl or platter.

Note to Cooks

If you enjoy an even stronger taste of ginger, try adding 1 or 2 teaspoons of ginger purée (paste) to the vegetables when you add them to the pan to cook.

EXOTIC RICE

Serves 2

Metric/Imperial		*American*
3 tbsp	olive oil	3 tbsp
30g/1oz	flaked/slivered almonds	¼ cup
30g/1oz	pine nuts	¼ cup
455g/1lb	cooked brown rice (page 36)	2½ cups
90ml/3fl oz	water	⅓ cup
30g/1oz	sultanas/golden seedless raisins or raisins	¼ cup
½ tsp	ground cinnamon	½ tsp
small pinch	ground cloves	small pinch
2 twists	freshly ground black pepper	2 twists
to taste	salt substitute	to taste

1. Heat the oil in a large frying pan, then add the almonds and pine nuts. Cook for no more than 2 minutes, watching and stirring all the time as they burn easily.
2. Carefully add the rice to the pan together with the water and the remaining ingredients, apart from the pepper and salt substitute.
3. Allow the mixture to cook for approximately 1½ to 2 minutes, shaking the pan or stirring constantly so it cooks evenly and does not stick.
4. Remove the pan from the heat and season with the pepper and salt substitute and serve.

STUFFED MARROW

Serves 4

Metric/Imperial		*American*
1 large (approx. 900g/2lb)	marrow	1 large (approx. 2lb)
240ml/8fl oz	olive/vegetable oil	1 cup
225g/8oz	onion, finely chopped	2 cups
30g/1oz	spring onions/scallions, chopped	¼ cup
55g/2oz	fresh dill and parsley, chopped	2 cups
1 tbsp	ginger purée/paste	1 tbsp
pinch	cayenne pepper	pinch
6 twists	freshly ground black pepper	6 twists
to taste	salt substitute	to taste
285g/10oz	mixed ground nuts	5 cups
55g/2oz	pine nuts	½ cup
85g/3oz	wholemeal/wholewheat breadcrumbs	1½ cups
2	egg whites, lightly beaten	2
680g/1½lb	sweet potatoes, optional	1½lb
425ml/15fl oz	water	2 cups

1. Wash the marrow and remove approximately 2cm (¾in) from each end, setting these pieces on one side. Then scoop out the core containing the seeds, leaving the flesh intact.
2. Meanwhile, heat half the oil in a saucepan and lightly sauté the onions, spring onions (scallions), herbs, ginger, cayenne and seasoning.
3. Remove the pan from the heat and add the ground nuts, pine nuts, breadcrumbs and egg whites. Mix all these ingredients together thoroughly.
4. Using a spoon, stuff the mixture into the marrow, packing it firmly, then replace the ends, using wooden cocktail sticks (toothpicks) to hold them in place.
5. Place the marrow in an ovenproof baking dish.
6. If using, peel and chop the sweet potatoes into 4-cm (1½-in) thick slices and pack these around the marrow.
7. Preheat the oven to 200°C/400°F/gas mark 6.
8. Pour the remainder of the olive oil and the water around the marrow. Cover the dish with kitchen (aluminium) foil and bake in the preheated oven. After 30 minutes' cooking, remove the foil and return the dish to the oven for the marrow to continue cooking, uncovered, until all the liquid has evaporated, approximately 1 hour.
9. Take out the cocktail sticks (toothpicks), then serve hot or cold.

GREEK ARTICHOKE STEW WITH TOFU

The addition of tofu (made from soya beans and full of protein) to this traditional Greek dish ensures that you have a complete protein meal. Serve it with wholemeal (wholewheat) bread and black olives for a Mediterranean experience.

Serves 4

Metric/Imperial		*American*
4	large globe artichokes (page 35)	4
170g/6oz	shallots	1½ cups
140g/5oz	carrots, sliced	1 cup
170g/6oz	spring onions/scallions, chopped	1 cup
225ml/8fl oz	olive/vegetable oil	1 cup
to taste	salt substitute	to taste
6 twists	freshly ground black pepper	6 twists
1 tbsp	plain/all-purpose wholemeal/wholewheat flour	1 tbsp
240ml/8fl oz	warm water	1 cup
1	lemon, juice of	1
170g/6oz	tofu, cubed	¾ cup
30g/1oz	fresh parsley	1 cup
30g/1oz	fresh dill	1 cup

1. Place the prepared vegetables in a large (non-stick if possible) saucepan and add the oil, salt substitute and pepper.
2. Mix the flour with the warm water and add this to the vegetables, ensuring that they are covered (just) with the water. Simmer over a medium heat, uncovered, until most of the water has evaporated.
3. Add the cubed tofu to the stew for the last few minutes of cooking so that it can absorb the flavours of the artichokes and herbs.
4. When all water has evaporated, remove the pan from the heat and place a double thickness of kitchen paper between the lid of the saucepan and the pan to absorb the steam as you get ready to serve.

STUFFED CABBAGE LEAVES

This outstandingly tasty dish also has enormous nutritional value. However, the sauce does contain egg yolks and so should be eaten only occasionally by anyone who is 'rotating' their intake of eggs (see the discussion on rotation in Chapter 2). This said, it is quite possible to enjoy these stuffed cabbage leaves without the accompanying sauce, so, if it's supposed to be an egg-free day but you really want to eat this dish, you still can!

Serves 4

Metric/Imperial		*American*
200g/7oz	brown rice, washed	1 cup
1 tbsp	currants	1 tbsp
55g/2oz	spring onions/scallions, chopped	½ cup
70g/2½oz	pine nuts	½ cup
5 twists	freshly ground black pepper	5 twists
to taste	salt substitute	to taste
1	egg white	1
45g/1½oz	ground almonds	½ cup
15g/½oz	fresh parsley, chopped	½ cup
1	large Savoy cabbage	1
210ml/7½fl oz	lemon juice	1 cup
1 quantity	Non-dairy Béchamel Sauce (page 43)	1 quantity
210ml/7½fl oz	olive oil	1 cup

1. Boil the washed rice for 8 minutes, drain and place in a mixing bowl.
2. Add the currants, spring onions (scallions), pine nuts, pepper, salt substitute, half the oil, the egg white, almonds and parsley. Mix these ingredients together well.
3. Boil the cabbage for 2 to 3 minutes to soften the outer leaves.
4. Remove from heat and separate the leaves. Place approximately 1 tablespoon of the nutty rice stuffing mixture at the centre of each leaf, then fold in the sides of the leaf to envelope this before placing each little package, folded over side down, in a non-stick saucepan.
5. When all the stuffing has been used, chop the remaining cabbage leaves and spread these on top of the cabbage parcels in the saucepan.
6. Place 2 small heatproof plates (saucers or side plates) on top of the chopped leaves to ensure that they stay in place during the cooking process.
7. Add the remaining oil and the lemon juice to the saucepan and then enough water to cover the contents.
8. Cover and bring to boil, then simmer gently for 30 to 40 minutes until, by tipping the saucepan you can see that there is no more than about a cupful of liquid remaining. Remove the pan from the heat and leave to stand while you make the Non-dairy Béchamel Sauce as given on page 43.

9. When the sauce is ready, pour it into the pan around the cabbage parcels, shaking the pan a little to encourage it round. Bring back to the boil, remove immediately and shake, then serve or you can serve them cold if you wish.
10. Alternatively, if no sauce is being made, allow the cabbage parcels to cook until almost all the liquid has evaporated. Remove the pan from the heat and serve or allow it to cool somewhat and serve at room temperature (ideally accompanied by other cooked vegetables such as beans and/or courgettes/zucchini).

SPINACH PIE WITH FETA OR COTTAGE CHEESE OR TOFU

This recipe can contain both a dairy product (feta or virtually fat-free cottage cheese) and eggs or, alternatively, egg whites only and tofu instead of the cheese if you are sensitive to dairy products and still want to enjoy a special creamy pie. The pie is equally good served with a salad or cooked vegetables.

Serves 4–6

Metric/Imperial		*American*
455g/1lb	feta or virtually fat-free cottage cheese or tofu	1lb
680g/1½lb	spinach, washed and finely chopped	1½lb
6 twists	freshly ground black pepper	6 twists
to taste	salt substitute	to taste
115g/4oz	onion, chopped	1 cup
120ml/4fl oz	olive/vegetable oil	½ cup
4	garlic cloves, chopped	4
30g/1oz	fresh dill	1 cup
30g/1oz	fresh parsley, chopped	1 cup
3	eggs or egg whites	3
50g/16oz	soya milk	⅓ cup
2 quantities	Shortcrust/Pie Pastry (page 38)	2 quantities
55g/2oz	spring onions/scallions, chopped	½ cup

1. Preheat the oven to 190°C/375°F/gas mark 5.
2. Crumble the feta or tofu. If using cottage cheese or tofu, lay it out on kitchen paper to drain off the excess liquid.
3. Place the spinach and most of the pepper and salt substitute in a frying pan, together with the onions, oils, garlic, dill and parsley, and allow to cook gently until the liquid has evaporated. Then, remove the pan from the heat and allow to cool.
4. In a bowl, beat the whole eggs or egg whites and add a little pepper and salt substitute. Add and mix in the feta, cottage cheese or tofu.
5. Add the soya milk and mix well before adding the spinach and herb mixture and mixing it in. Check that the seasoning is to your taste and decide whether or not additional pepper and/or salt substitute is required.
6. Roll out the pastry and use it to line a oiled deep 20-cm (8-in) pie dish. Pile the spinach mixture into the dish and smooth the top with the back of a spoon. Seal the edges and pierce the top. Use the remaining pastry to cover the top of the pie and score the surface into portion-sizes.
7. Put the pie into the preheated oven and bake until the pastry starts to turn golden brown on top (30 to 40 minutes). Serve hot or at room temperature.

MUSHROOM PIE

As with some other recipes in this section, we have provided the option of replacing the usual dairy product (feta or cottage cheese) with tofu. Also, egg whites can be used instead of whole eggs. These options are not meant to suggest that the cheese and whole egg choices are 'bad', simply that for some people they may not be the best choice and that there are other options to choose from if you wish.

This pie tastes good with either salad or cooked vegetables.

Serves 4

Metric/Imperial		*American*
225g/8oz	feta or cottage cheese or tofu	1 cup
455g/1lb	firm mushrooms	1lb
170g/6oz	carrots, sliced	1½ cups
225g/8oz	Spanish or spring onions/scallions, chopped	2 cups
15g/½oz	fresh, parsley	½ cup
15g/½oz	fresh dill	½ cup
210ml/7½fl oz	water	1 cup
210ml/7½fl oz	olive/vegetable oil	1 cup
4	eggs or egg whites, beaten	4
pinch	cayenne pepper	pinch
5 twists	freshly ground black pepper	5 twists
1 quantity	Shortcrust/Pie Pastry (page 38)	1 quantity

1. Crumble the feta or tofu. If using cottage cheese or tofu, place it on kitchen paper to drain off the excess liquid.
2. Wipe the mushrooms and chop them into thick slices, then place them in a saucepan together with the carrots, onion, parsley, dill, water and oil.
3. Heat gently, stirring, until the liquid is simmering, at which time cover and allow to cook until the liquid has disappeared.
4. Remove the pan from the heat and allow to cool slightly before adding in the beaten eggs or whites and the feta or cottage cheese or tofu. Mix well.
5. Roll out the pastry and use it to line an oiled pie dish. Pile the mushroom mixture into the lined pie dish. Smooth the top of the mixture with the back of a spoon. Use the remaining pastry to cover the top of the pie and score the surface into portion-sizes. Seal the edges and pierce the top.
6. Preheat the oven to 190°C/375°F/gas mark 5.
7. Put the pie into the preheated oven and bake until the pastry starts to turn golden brown on top (30 to 40 minutes). Serve hot or at room temperature.

CABBAGE RISOTTO

Serve with wholemeal (wholewheat) toast for an excellent, complete protein light meal.

Serves 2–3

Metric/Imperial		*American*
215g/7½ oz	olive/vegetable oil	1 cup
450g/1lb	green soft cabbage, shredded	4 cups
4	garlic cloves, sliced	4
340g/12oz	easy cook brown rice	1½ cups
115g/4oz	onion, chopped	1 cup
60g/2oz	celery, chopped	1 cup
2 tbsp	lemon juice	2 tbsp
5 twists	freshly ground black pepper	5 twists
to taste	salt substitute	to taste
170g/6oz	tofu, cubed, optional	⅔ cup

1. Place all the ingredients, except the tofu, if using, into a saucepan and add water to cover, just.
2. Cover and bring to the boil and allow to simmer over a medium heat until all the water has evaporated or been absorbed by the rice, approximately 45 minutes. If tofu is being used, add it 10 minutes before the end of cooking, when the water has almost all gone.

12

Main Meals with Fish

BAKED SARDINES

Sardines are among the best foods for people with arthritis as they contain ample quantities of the EPA oils which are so helpful in counteracting excessive inflammation. This is in addition to the many other benefits they offer, helping as they do to prevent heart disease and make the immune system efficient.

You can make this dish with whitebait instead of sardines, simply double the number you use.

Serve with one of the salads included in this book to complete your meal.

Serves 2

Metric/Imperial		*American*
10	medium sardines	10
to taste	salt substitute	to taste
1	large onion, cut into rings	1
5 twists	freshly ground black pepper	5 twists
1 tsp	dried oregano	1 tsp
240ml/8fl oz	olive oil	1 cup
6	garlic cloves, halved lengthwise	6
pinch	cayenne pepper	pinch
240ml/8fl oz	water	1 cup

1. Preheat the oven to 200°C/350°F/gas mark 4.
2. Wash and clean the fish and sprinkle salt substitute over them. Place them in a dish and cover with foil or clingfilm (plastic wrap) and refrigerate for 1 hour.
3. After the hour has passed, lay half the onion rings in a layer over the base of an ovenproof dish, season with some black pepper, half the oregano and the salt substitute and drizzle half the olive oil over, then lay the sardines on top. Cover the fish with the remaining onion rings and the garlic, cayenne, the rest of the black pepper, salt substitute to taste and then drizzle over the remaining olive oil and sprinkle over the rest of the oregano.
4. Add the water and bake in the preheated oven until the liquid has evaporated (approximately 35 to 45 minutes).

GRILLED (BROILED) SARDINES

This dish is best served with a simple green leaf or other fresh salad of your choice.

Serves 2

Metric/Imperial		*American*
1 tbsp	dried oregano	1 tbsp
3 tbsp	lemon juice	3 tbsp
4 tbsp	olive oil	4 tbsp
to taste	salt substitute	to taste
2 twists	freshly ground black pepper	2 twists
12	sardines	12

1. Mix the oregano, lemon juice, olive oil and salt and pepper together well in a cup or screw-top jar.
2. Remove and discard the heads from the fish and scrape off the scales.
3. Place the fish in a dish and pour over the dressing. Refrigerate for 1 hour.
4. After the hour has passed, cover the grill (broiler) pan with kitchen (aluminium) foil and place the sardines side by side on it and cook under a hot grill (broiler). Keep the marinade to hand.
5. After 10 minutes' cooking, spoon a little of the marinade over the fish.
6. After 5 more minutes, turn the fish, cook for 15 minutes and serve.

BAKED SALMON

Salmon is one of the fish richest in the oils helpful in reducing the inflammatory processes at work in arthritis. So, help your body a little and enjoy the taste of this dish, too, serving it with a side salad or cooked courgettes (zucchini) and carrots.

Serves 2

Metric/Imperial		*American*
4 tbsp	olive oil	4 tbsp
2 tbsp	lemon juice	2 tbsp
1 tsp	dried oregano	1 tsp
2	garlic cloves, crushed	2
4 twists	freshly ground black pepper	4 twists
pinch	cayenne pepper	pinch
to taste	salt substitute	to taste
2	salmon steaks	2

1. Preheat the oven to 190°C/375°F/gas mark 5.
2. Put the olive oil, lemon juice, oregano, garlic, cayenne, pepper and salt to taste in a cup or screw-top jar and mix well.
3. Wash and pat dry the salmon steaks and place them in a baking dish.
4. Pour the dressing over the fish and turn them several times to ensure that all sides are well covered with it.
5. Bake the fish in the preheated oven for 20 to 30 minutes.

POACHED COD WITH GARLIC AND LEMON

Cod, like salmon and sardines, contains the kinds of oils that help reduce the inflammatory processes in arthritis.

You can use salmon steaks or fillets in place of the cod if you wish or for a change. Either way, the perfect accompaniments are a side salad and/or cooked vegetables dressed with lemon juice and olive oil.

Serves 2

Metric/Imperial		*American*
2	cod steaks or fillets	2
to taste	salt substitute	to taste
90ml/3fl oz	olive oil	⅓ cup
3 tbsp	lemon juice	3 tbsp
2	garlic cloves, crushed	2
4 twists	freshly ground black pepper	4 twists
pinch	cayenne pepper	pinch

1. Wash the cod and pat it dry. Put it on a plate and sprinkle a little salt substitute on both sides, cover with kitchen (aluminium) foil and refrigerate for 1 hour.
2. Mix the remaining ingredients together in a cup or screw-top jar.

3. Take a saucepan that the fish will easily fit into side by side and, judging by eye, pour sufficient water into the pan to cover the fish (how much you need will depend on the size of the saucepan and the thickness of the fish pieces). Add a pinch or 2 of salt substitute and bring the water to the boil.
4. When the water is boiling, place the fish in it, check that it is completely covered and allow to simmer for 10 to 15 minutes (the longer time for cod steaks and the shorter time for cod fillets).
5. Remove the fish from the pan with a fish slice, draining off all the water, and serve pouring the dressing over.

BAKED COD WITH ASPARAGUS

Serves 2

Metric/Imperial		*American*
4 tbsp	olive oil	4 tbsp
3 tbsp	lemon juice	3 tbsp
1	garlic clove, crushed	1
1 tsp	dried oregano	1 tsp
pinch	cayenne pepper	pinch
½ tsp	salt substitute	½ tsp
6 twists	freshly ground black pepper	6 twists
2	thick cod steaks	2
2	baby courgettes/zucchini, halved lengthwise	2
10	asparagus spears	10

1. Preheat the oven to 190°C/375°F/gas mark 5.
2. Mix the oil, lemon juice, garlic, oregano, cayenne, salt and pepper together in a small bowl or screw-top jar.
3. Wash and pat dry the cod steaks and place them in a baking dish.
4. Surround the steaks with the asparagus and courgettes (zucchini).
5. Pour the dressing over the fish and vegetables and turn the fish to ensure that all sides are covered with the dressing.
6. Bake in the preheated oven for approximately 20 minutes.

GREY MULLET WITH LEMON

Serves 2

Metric/Imperial		*American*
2	grey mullet	2
to taste	salt substitute	to taste
5	garlic cloves, chopped	5
170g/6oz	carrots, cut lengthwise	6oz
200ml/7fl oz	lemon juice	scant cup
200ml/7fl oz	olive oil	1 cup
425ml/15fl oz	water	2 cups
30g/1oz	fresh parsley, chopped	½ cup
4 twists	freshly ground black pepper	4 twists

1. Wash and clean the fish.
2. Pat them dry and place them on a plate. Sprinkle a little salt substitute over them and then half the lemon juice. Turn the fish to ensure they are well dressed with the lemon juice, then cover the plate with kitchen (aluminum) foil and refrigerate for 45 minutes.
3. Place the fish in a deep frying pan and add all the remaining ingredients.
4. Bring to the boil, then allow to simmer, shaking the pan gently from time to time, until all the water has evaporated (approximately 30 to 45 minutes).

BAKED HADDOCK (OR COD) AND MUSHROOMS

Haddock is rich in the fish oils that can help people with arthritic or other inflammatory conditions.

This dish only needs a crisp side salad to make a complete meal.

Serves 2

Metric/Imperial	*American*	
115g/4oz	celery, sliced	1 cup
1 tbsp	chives, chopped	1 tbsp
210ml/7½fl oz	Vegetable Broth (page 80)	1 cup
2	haddock or cod fillets	2
2 pinches	paprika	2 pinches
2 pinches	salt substitute	2 pinches
115g/4oz	button mushrooms, coarsely chopped	1 cup
2 tbsp	olive oil	2 tbsp

1. Preheat the oven to 190°C/375°F/gas mark 5.
2. Cook the celery and the chives in the Vegetable Broth for 5 minutes, then purée the mixture in a food processor or blender.
3. Place the haddock or cod fillets in an oiled ovenproof dish, add the paprika and salt substitute, then cover with the celery and chive mixture.
4. Arrange the mushrooms around the fish and pour 1 tablespoon of the olive oil over each of the fish.
5. Bake in the preheated oven for 15 to 30 minutes.

FISH CHOWDER

This fish soup is a meal in itself. Which fish you choose is up to you – anything from cod to shrimps or lobster or a mixture all taste good.

Serves 3

Metric/Imperial		*American*
900g/2lb	fish fillets or seafood of your choosing	2lb
2 tbsp	olive oil	2 tbsp
2	garlic cloves, peeled	2
2	onions, chopped	2
2	carrots, chopped	2
570ml/1pt	Garlic Broth (page 82)	3 cups
210ml/7½fl oz	tinned unsalted tomato juice or extra Garlic Broth	1 cup
3 tbsp	sesame seeds, toasted and ground	3 tbsp
210ml/7½fl oz	dry white wine	1 cup
2 tbsp	fresh parsley, chopped	2 tbsp
1 tsp	dried basil	1 tsp
1 tsp	dried thyme	1 tsp
½ tsp	paprika	½ tsp
½ tsp	cumin	½ tsp

1. Put the olive oil, garlic, onions and carrots into a saucepan and sauté for 5 minutes.
2. Add the Garlic Broth, the tomato juice, if using, or, if not, the extra Garlic Broth, the sesame seeds, wine and herbs and spices (reserving a pinch or 2 of the parsley for garnishing later) to the vegetables and bring to the boil.
3. Allow the soup to gently simmer for 1 hour, partly covered.
4. Cut the fish into large pieces and, after the hour, add the fish and cook for a further 10 to 15 minutes.
5. Serve, garnished with the reserved parsley.

13

Main Meals with Chicken and Turkey

CHICKEN WITH GINGER AND GARLIC

There are only a few poultry recipes in this book. This is not because we have anything particular against eating chicken, turkey or any other birds, but because we feel that the emphasis should be on fish and vegetarian meals with poultry being eaten only periodically.

When you do eat chicken, if at all possible, make it free-range and ensure it has not been exposed to antibiotic or steroid medication during their rearing. Also, avoid all the fat, which means buy skinless pieces to cook.

You can serve this dish with any vegetables or fresh salads you like, but a rice-based side dish is particularly to be recommended.

Serves 2

Metric/Imperial		*American*
455g/1lb	boneless, skinless chicken thighs	1lb
140ml/5fl oz	olive oil	⅔ cup
5	garlic cloves	5
85g/3oz	root ginger, freshly grated	½ cup
140ml/5fl oz	dry white wine	⅔ cup
pinch	cayenne pepper	pinch
5 twists	freshly ground black pepper	5 twists
to taste	salt substitute	to taste
685ml/24fl oz	hot water	3 cups

1. Wash the chicken thighs well.
2. Pat them dry and place them in a deep frying pan together with the olive oil.
3. Heat gently and stir frequently for 10 to 15 minutes, then add all the remaining ingredients except the water and cook, stirring constantly for 1 minute.
4. Add 500ml (16fl oz/2 cups) of the hot water and cover, allowing the contents to simmer gently until the water has almost all evaporated, approximately 30 to 40 minutes. Then add the remaining hot water and cook for a further 10 minutes.

TURKEY FILLETS WITH MUSHROOMS AND HERBS

Simply serve this dish with a side salad for a perfect meal.

Serves 2

Metric/Imperial		*American*
455g/1lb	turkey fillets	1lb
115g/4oz	button or shiitaki mushrooms	1 cup
2 tbsp	lemon juice	2 tbsp
140ml/5fl oz	olive/vegetable oil	⅔ cup
1 tsp	dried oregano	1 tsp
1 tsp	dried thyme	1 tsp
pinch	cayenne pepper	pinch
to taste	salt substitute	to taste
340ml/12fl oz	warm water	1½ cups

1. Preheat the oven to 190°C/350°F/gas mark 5.
2. Wash the turkey fillets and pat them dry.
3. Lay the fillets in the base of an ovenproof baking dish.
4. Wipe the mushrooms (if using shiitaki mushrooms, discard the stalks) and place them around the turkey in the dish.
5. Add all the remaining ingredients, except the warm water, ensuring that the turkey and mushrooms are completely coated with the herbs and lemon juice and oil.
6. Add the warm water.

7. Cover the dish with kitchen (aluminium) foil and bake in the preheated oven for 50 minutes.
8. When the hour has passed, reduce the oven temperature to 170°C/325°F/gas mark 3, remove the foil, bake for a further 20 minutes.

ROAST CHICKEN WITH HERBS AND GARLIC

Ideal accompaniments for this dish are a side salad or a rice side dish.

Serves 2

Metric/Imperial		*American*
455g/1lb	skinless chicken portions, either quarters or breast fillets	1lb
5	garlic cloves, chopped	5
1 tbsp	dried thyme or oregano	1 tbsp
1½ tbsp	lemon juice	1½ tbsp
285g/10oz	fennel bulb, cleaned and quartered	10oz
5 twists	freshly ground black pepper	5 twists
140ml/5fl oz	olive/vegetable oil	⅔ cup
340ml/12fl oz	warm water	1½ cups

1. Preheat the oven to 190°C/350°F/gas mark 5.
2. Wash the chicken and pat it dry.
3. Lay the chicken in an ovenproof baking dish with the fennel.
4. Add all the remaining ingredients, except the water, mix, then pour the water over.
5. Cover the dish with kitchen (aluminium) foil and bake in the preheated oven for 30 minutes.
6. After this time has passed, remove the foil and allow to cook for a further 20 minutes, or until all the liquid has evaporated.

14

Desserts

COCONUT COOKIES

Makes approximately 25 cookies

Metric/Imperial		*American*
2 tbsp	olive or safflower oil	2 tbsp
360g/12¾oz	desiccated/shredded coconut	4 cups
2 tbsp	soya milk	2 tbsp
10 tbsp	rice syrup (brown)	10 tbsp

1. Preheat the oven to 180°C/350°F/gas mark 4 and use the oil to grease a large baking tray (cookie sheet).
2. Place the coconut in a bowl and add the soya milk and mix together thoroughly before adding the rice syrup. Continue to mix by hand until the texture is even.
3. Mould spoonfuls of the mixture into individual balls, approximately 4cm (1½in) in diameter, and place these on the prepared baking tray (cookie sheet).

4. Bake in the preheated oven for approximately 15 minutes, or until the cookies are just beginning to brown.
5. Allow to cool before transferring to an airtight storage container. Eat within a few days.

VEGAN RICE PUDDING

Serves 3

Metric/Imperial		*American*
455g/1lb	cooked rice (page 36)	2½ cups
2 tsp	arrowroot	2 tsp
240ml/8fl oz	soya or rice milk, unsweetened	1 cup
3 tbsp	rice syrup	3 tbsp
3 tbsp	raisins	3 tbsp
1 tsp	cinnamon, to decorate	1 tsp

1. While the rice is still soft, moist and hot, place it in a saucepan.
2. Mix the arrowroot into the soya milk and add this and the remaining ingredients, except the cinnamon, to the rice and mix well.
3. Bring to the boil and simmer for a few minutes until it thickens, stirring periodically to prevent it burning or sticking.
4. Spoon the pudding into serving bowls and sprinkle the cinnamon over each serving to decorate.

QUINCE WITH NUTS AND HONEY

This winter dessert derives from those climes where quinces grow freely – Southern Europe. This long-neglected fruit is now generally, but seasonally available (in the late autumn and early winter months) from specialist greengrocers and ethnic stores. If a large quince is chosen, this dish can often become a meal in itself.

The honey, nuts and yogurt cut any sharpness in taste of the quince in much the same way as brown sugar and raisins do in baked apple dishes. Although the yogurt is very good with the baked quince, do not add it if you have any sensitivity to dairy foods.

Serves 1

Metric/Imperial		*American*
1	medium to large quince	1
2 tsp	honey	2 tsp
85g/3oz	fresh shelled walnuts	1 cup
30g/1oz	low- or virtually no fat, natural/plain, live yogurt	⅛ cup

1. Preheat the oven to 150°C/300°F/gas mark 2.
2. Wash the quince well and bake it in the preheated oven for 45 minutes to 1 hour.
3. Halve the quince, removing the core and seeds.
4. Spoon the honey over the hot fruit so it melts.
5. Serve with the nuts (which complement the taste wonderfully well) and, if desired, the yogurt.

SWEET PUMPKIN PIE

Serves 10

Metric/Imperial		*American*
900g/2lb	prepared pumpkin, grated	2lb
pinch	salt substitute	pinch
140g/5oz	rice flakes	1 cup
140g/5oz	ground almonds	1 cup
140g/5oz	walnuts, chopped	1 cup
140g/5oz	sultanas/golden seedless raisins, washed and dried	1 cup
340ml/12fl oz	honey	1½ cups
1 tbsp	cinnamon	1 tbsp
1	packet filo pastry, defrosted	1
90ml/3fl oz	olive/vegetable oil	½ cup

1. Remove the seeds from the pumpkin, peel and coarsely grate the flesh.
2. Place the grated pumpkin in a colander and sprinkle the salt substitute over it. Mix it in well and allow it to drain for 2 hours.
3. Preheat the oven to 170°C/325°F/gas mark 3.
4. Squeeze the surplus liquid from the pumpkin with your hands, then transfer the pumpkin to a bowl.
5. Add the rice flakes, almond flour, walnuts, sultanas (golden seedless raisins), honey and cinnamon. Mix all of these together well.
6. Line a large square or rectangular baking dish with filo pastry, brushing with oil, then repeat twice more.

7. Pile the pumpkin mixture into the lined dish and smooth the top with the back of a spoon.
8. Lay a layer of filo pastry over the top of the pie, brush with oil, then repeat twice more, brushing the top of the pie with oil.
9. With a sharp knife, score the top of the pie with a grid to show the portions.
10. Bake in the preheated oven until the top of the pie is golden brown (approximately 50 minutes). Serve hot or cold.

SPECIALLY STEWED DRIED FRUIT

The stewing of dried fruit would seemingly not require cooking instructions. However, this variation justifies a recipe here as it uses particular potassium-rich fruits (potassium is important in relieving the symptoms of arthritis) and an unusual method of rehydration.

Organic dried fruits are available, as are sun-dried fruits. These are the types that you should use, if possible, rather than commercially produced dried fruit as the latter is sulphur-dried. The fruit most in line with the nutritional emphasis of this dish would be Hunza dried wild apricots, which are to be found in specialist health-food shops.

This dessert may be served hot, at room temperature or cold from the refrigerator, with a spoonful of live, natural (plain) yogurt or on its own, as you please.

Serves 4 to 6

Metric/Imperial		*American*
455g/1lb	mixed dried fruit (organic, sun-dried if possible, particularly peaches, apricots and raisins and/or sultanas/golden seedless raisins*	1lb
500ml/16fl oz	pure peach or grape juice*	2 cups
240ml/8fl oz	natural/plain, live, yogurt, optional, to serve	1 cup

1. Wash the dried fruit thoroughly to remove all dust and, if you are not using organic fruit, any surface chemicals used in the drying process.
2. Place the fruit in a saucepan with the peach or grape juice and allow to stand for 2 hours.
3. Then, bring to the boil and simmer gently for 15 to 20 minutes, until the liquid has significantly reduced and the fruit is soft.

* Peaches, apricots and grapes are extremely rich in potassium.

STEWED FRESH FRUIT

Serves 1

Metric/Imperial		*America*
1	quince, large pear or cooking apple, peeled, cored and quartered	1
8 to 10	cloves	8 to 10
1 tbsp	honey	1 tbsp
1 tsp	lemon juice*	1 tsp
1 tbsp	pine nuts	1 tbsp

1. Prick the fruit and insert at least 2 cloves into each fruit quarter.
2. Place the fruit, honey and lemon juice in a saucepan and just cover with water.
3. Bring to the boil and allow to simmer until the fruit has softened (approximately 20 minutes).
4. Serve the fruit warm or cold, sprinkling the pine nuts over just before serving.

* The lemon juice is used to help the fruit retain its natural colour, to prevent oxidation and browning.

Index

Alkmini's dairy-free sandwich 96–7
artichoke and herb stew 128

baked cod with asparagus 150
baked haddock (or cod) and mushrooms 152
baked head of garlic, Chicago-style 91–2
baked salmon 147
baked sardines 144–5
bean soup 87–8
bean stew 98–9
Béchamel sauce, non-dairy 43
Boris's mint and honey salad dressing 53–4
butter (lima) bean roast 112–13
butter (lima) bean salad 64–5

cabbage, cauliflower and avocado salad 57–8
cabbage risotto 143
celeriac and carrots with ginger 89–90
celery salad, Middle Eastern 59–60
chicken with ginger and garlic 155–6
chickpea (garbanzo) and ginger salad 61–2
classic lentil soup 85–6
coconut cookies 160–61
countryside vegetable soup 83–4
courgette (zucchini) cakes or loaf with almonds 108–9
courgettes (zucchini) with carrots and ginger 95
couscous with almonds and pine nuts 101–2

exotic pomegranate and passion fruit breakfast 44–5
exotic rice 131

fish chowder 153–4

garlic broth 82
garlic and cider vinegar dressing 56
globe artichokes, preparation 35–6
Greek artichoke stew with tofu 134–5

green leaf and herb salad 68
green peasant salad and dressing 66–7
grey mullet with lemon 151
grilled (broiled) sardines 146

high-fibre millet, oats and fruit breakfast 52
hummus 74–6

leek pie with tofu 126–7
leek and rice stew 121
lentil and nut roast 114–16
lentil soup 85–6

Mediterranean chickpea (garbanzo) salad 63
Middle Eastern celery salad 59–60
millet, oats and fruit breakfast 52
mixed vegetable cooked salad 69–70
mushroom and nut roast 117–18
mushroom pie 141–2
mushroom sauce 40–41
mushrooms with garlic and ginger 100

non-dairy Béchamel sauce 43

omelette 50
orange salad 73

pasta with olives and garlic 110–11
pastry 38–9
pine nut and almond pesto sauce 41–2
poached cod with garlic and lemon 148–9
pomegranate and passion fruit breakfast 44–5
pomegranate and wheat breakfast 51

quince with nuts and honey 163

rice, exotic 131
rice, preparation 36–8
roast chicken with herbs and garlic 159
root salad 71–2

savoury pumpkin pie 105–7
shortcrust pastry 38–9
spaghetti with peas 122–3
specially stewed dried fruit 166–7
spicy dressing 55
spinach pie with feta or cottage cheese or tofu 139–40
spinach and rice with dill and garlic 119–20
stewed fresh fruit 168
stir-fried tofu with ginger, vegetables and nuts 129–30
Stone Age breakfast 46–7
stuffed cabbage leaves 136–8
stuffed cannelloni 124–5
stuffed marrow 132–3
stuffed onions 93–4
sweet potatoes with mushrooms 103–4
sweet pumpkin pie 164–5
Swiss power breakfast 48–9

turkey fillets with mushrooms and herbs 157–8
Tzatzicki 77–8

vegan rice pudding 162
vegetable broth 80–81

walnut and garlic dip 79